The LITTLE BLACK BOOK *of*

Published by
Hal Leonard

Order No. HLE90004563
ISBN 978-1-78038-795-6

Printed in the EU.

All-Time GREATEST HITS

★★★★

AIN'T NO MOUNTAIN HIGH ENOUGH
Diana Ross...12

ALRIGHT
Supergrass...6

ARE YOU GONNA GO MY WAY
Lenny Kravitz...8

AVALON
Roxy Music...10

BABY, COME BACK
The Equals...18

BACK FOR GOOD
Take That...20

BAD DAY
Daniel Powter...15

BECAUSE OF YOU
Kelly Clarkson...22

BIG LOVE
Fleetwood Mac...24

BLACK NIGHT
Deep Purple...26

BORN TO DIE
Lana Del Rey...28

BRIGHT EYES
Art Garfunkel...34

CAN'T GET YOU OUT OF MY HEAD
Kylie Minogue...36

CRY
Godley & Creme...38

DANCING IN THE STREET
Martha & The Vandellas...40

THE DARK END OF THE STREET
James Carr...42

DO YOU REALIZE??
The Flaming Lips...44

DREAM LOVER
Bobby Darin...46

EASY
Commodores...48

ENJOY THE SILENCE
Depeche Mode...50

ENOLA GAY
Orchestral Manoeuvres In The Dark...31

EVERLASTING LOVE
Love Affair...52

GALVESTON
Glen Campbell...54

GENO
Dexy's Midnight Runners...56

GROOVIN'
The Young Rascals...58

HALFWAY TO PARADISE
Billy Fury...60

HEARTBREAK HOTEL
Elvis Presley...62

HOUNDS OF LOVE
Kate Bush...64

I CAN HELP
Billy Swan...66

I DON'T FEEL LIKE DANCIN'
Scissor Sisters...68

I NEVER LOVED A MAN (THE WAY I LOVE YOU)
Aretha Franklin...74

I ONLY HAVE EYES FOR YOU
The Flamingos...76

I WANT YOU BACK
The Jackson 5...71

I'M WAITING FOR THE MAN
The Velvet Underground...78

JUST MY IMAGINATION (RUNNING AWAY WITH ME)
The Temptations...80

KARMA CHAMELEON
Culture Club...82

LAST TRAIN TO CLARKSVILLE
The Monkees...85

LIFE ON MARS?
David Bowie...88

THE LOOK OF LOVE
ABC...90

LOVE REALLY HURTS WITHOUT YOU
Billy Ocean...94

LUCKY MAN
The Verve...96

ME AND BOBBY McGEE
Janis Joplin...99

MISS YOU
The Rolling Stones...102

MONEY (THAT'S WHAT I WANT)
The Beatles...106

MOVIN' ON UP
Primal Scream...112

MR. BLUE SKY
Electric Light Orchestra...114

MY BABY JUST CARES FOR ME
Nina Simone...118

MY GIRL
Madness...120

THE NIGHT
Frankie Valli & The Four Seasons...109

PERFECT DAY
Lou Reed...122

PLEASE MR. POSTMAN
The Marvelettes...124

REHAB
Amy Winehouse...130

ROLLING IN THE DEEP
Adele...127

SENSES WORKING OVERTIME
XTC...132

SHAKIN' ALL OVER
Johnny Kidd & The Pirates...138

SIGN YOUR NAME
Terence Trent D'Arby...140

SIR DUKE
Stevie Wonder...135

SOLSBURY HILL
Peter Gabriel...142

STARS
Simply Red...145

STEADY, AS SHE GOES
The Raconteurs...148

THE SUBURBS
Arcade Fire...151

THERE GOES THE FEAR
Doves...154

THIS AIN'T A LOVE SONG
Scouting For Girls...157

THIS OLD HEART OF MINE (IS WEAK FOR YOU)
The Isley Brothers...160

TONIGHT'S THE NIGHT
Rod Stewart...162

THE TRACKS OF MY TEARS
The Miracles...164

UP ON THE ROOF
The Drifters...166

VALERIE
The Zutons...168

WARWICK AVENUE
Duffy...170

WE GOTTA GET OUT OF THIS PLACE
The Animals...173

WHAT'S GOING ON
Marvin Gaye...176

WHIP IT
Devo...178

WHOLE LOTTA SHAKIN' GOIN' ON
Jerry Lee Lewis...180

WILD THING
The Troggs...182

WILL YOU LOVE ME TOMORROW
The Shirelles...184

YOU CAN'T HURRY LOVE
The Supremes...190

YOU TO ME ARE EVERYTHING
The Real Thing...186

YOU'VE LOST THAT LOVIN' FEELIN'
The Righteous Brothers...188

Alright

Words & Music by Gareth Coombes, Daniel Goffey & Michael Quinn

D Em F♯m F A G Dm/F

Intro | D | D | D | D ||

Verse 1

D
We are young, we run green, keep our teeth nice and clean,
           Em   D
See our friends, see the sights, feel al - right.

We wake up, we go out, smoke a fag, put it out,
           Em   D
See our friends, see the sights, feel al - right.

Chorus 1

F♯m   F
   Are we like you? I can't be sure
           Em   A
Of the scene as she turns, we are strange in our worlds.

Verse 2

(Em)   D
But we are young, we get by, can't go mad, ain't got time,
               Em   D
Sleep a - round, if we like, but we're al - right.

Got some cash, bought some wheels, took it out, 'cross the fields,
               Em   D
Lost con - trol, hit a wall, but we're al - right.

Chorus 2 As Chorus 1

Verse 3

```
(Em)         D
But we are young, we run green, keep our teeth nice and clean,
          Em                                D
See our friends, see the sights, feel al - right.
```

Instrumental

```
| G      | Dm/F   | G      | Dm/F   |
| G      | Dm/F   | G      | Dm/F   |
| Em     | A      ||
|: D     | D      | D      | D      |
| Em     | Em     | D      | D      :|
```

Chorus 3 As Chorus 1

Verse 4 As Verse 3

Outro

```
| D      | D      | D      | D      |
| Em     | Em     | D      | D      ||  To fade
```

Are You Gonna Go My Way

Words by Lenny Kravitz
Music by Lenny Kravitz & Craig Ross

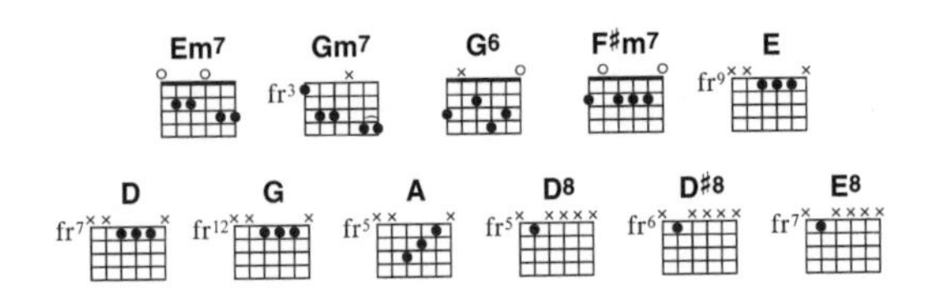

Em7 riff x8

Intro ‖: Em7 | Em7 :‖

Verse 1

Em7 riff
I was born, long ago

I am the chosen, I'm the one.

I have come, to save the day

And I won't leave until I'm done.

Gm7 riff
So that's why, we've got to try

We got to breathe and have some fun.

Em7 riff
Though I'm not paid, I play this game

And I won't stop until I'm done.

Chorus 1

G6 But what I really **F♯m7** want to know is **E D E**

Are you gonna go my **E** way? **G E**

G6 And I got to **F♯m7** got to know.

Em7 riff x4

‖: Em7 | Em7 :‖

Verse 2

Em7 riff
I don't know why, we always cry

This we must leave and get undone.

We must engage, and rearrange

And turn this planet back to one.

Gm7 riff
So tell me why, we got to die

And kill each other one by one.

Em7 riff
We've got to hug, and rub-a-dub

We've got to dance and be in love.

Chorus 2

G6 F♯m7 E D E
But what I really want to know is

E G E
Are you gonna go my way?

G6 F♯m7
And I got to got to know.

Instrumental

|: E D | D A D A :| *play 11 times*

| E D | D | D D8 D♯8 E8 |

Em7 riff, Em7 riff, Em7 riff, Em7 riff

| Em7 | Em7 | Em7 | Em7 | Em7 | Em7 | Em7 | Em7 |

| G6 | F♯m7 | G6 | F♯m7 |

Outro

E D E E G E
Are you gonna go my way?

G6 F♯m7
'Cause baby I got to know,

Yeah.

Avalon

Words & Music by Bryan Ferry

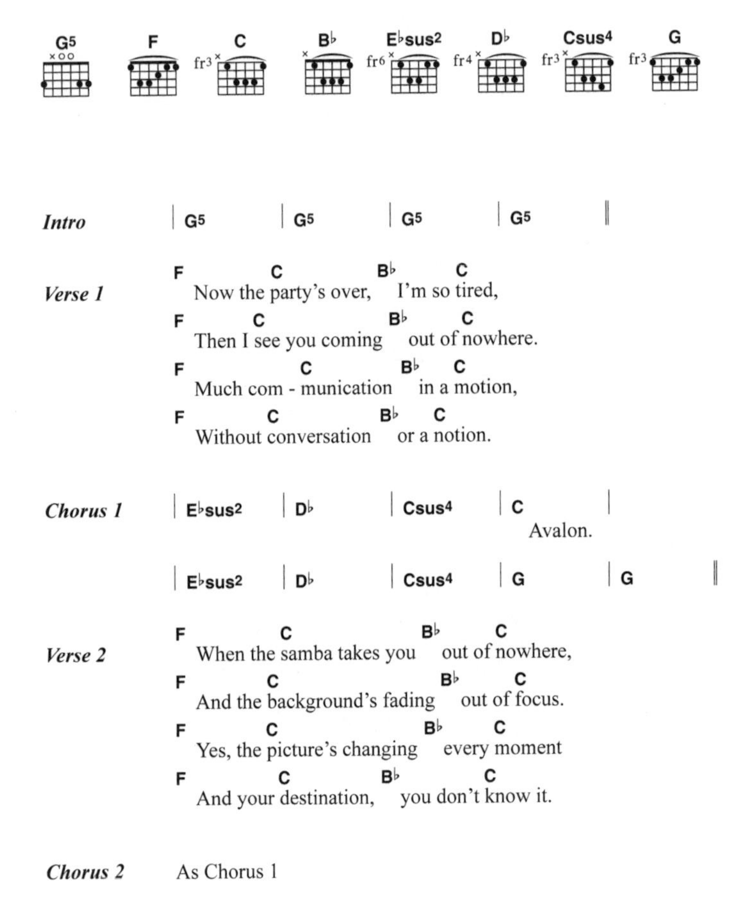

Bridge

| G | C | G | C |
| G | C | G | C ||

Ooh, ooh.______________________

```
G          C          G   C
Dancing, dancing.
G          C          G
Dancing, dancing.
```

Verse 3

```
F            C              B♭          C
   When you bossa nova,     there's no holding,
F             C                    B♭      C
   Would you have me dancing,     out of nowhere?
```

Chorus 3

| E♭sus2 | D♭ | Csus4 | C |
Avalon.

| E♭sus2 | D♭ | Csus4 | G |

| G | G ||

Instrumental

||: F | C | B♭ | C :||

Outro

||: F | C | B♭ | C :||
Avalon.

Play 11 times to fade

Ain't No Mountain High Enough

Words & Music by Nickolas Ashford & Valerie Simpson

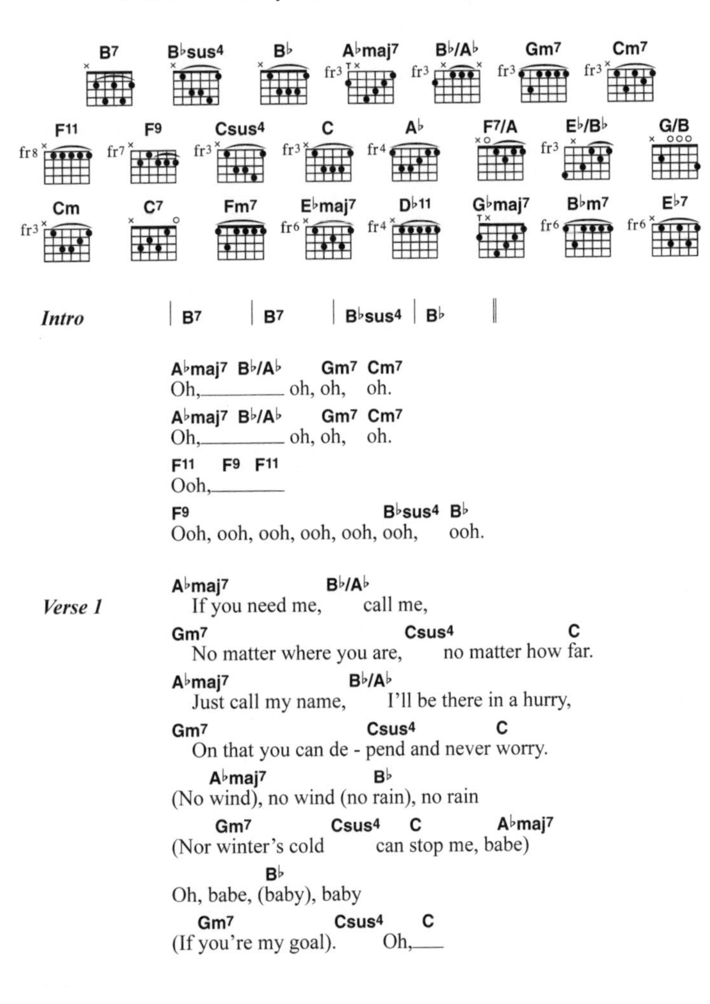

cont.

A♭maj7 B♭
(No wind), no wind (no rain), no rain

Gm7 Csus4 C
(Can stop me, babe) If you wanna go.______

Interlude

A♭maj7 B♭/A♭ Gm7 Cm7
Oh,__________ oh, oh, oh.

A♭maj7 B♭/A♭ Gm7 Cm7
Oh,__________ oh, oh, oh.

A♭maj7 B♭/A♭ Gm7 Cm7
Oh,__________ oh, oh, oh.

F11 F9 F11
Ooh,________

F9 B♭sus4 B♭
Ooh, ooh, ooh, ooh, ooh, ooh, ooh.

Verse 2

A♭ F7/A
I know, I know you must follow the sun

Wherever it leads, but remember,

E♭/B♭
If you should fall short of your desires

G/B Cm
Remember life holds for you one guarantee;

E♭/B♭ B♭ A♭
You'll always have me.

F7/A
And if you should miss my loving one of these old days

If you should ever miss the arms that used to hold you so close,

E♭/B♭ G/B
Or the lips that used to touch yours so tenderly,

Cm C7
Just re - member what I told you the day I set you free.

Chorus 1

A♭maj7
(Ain't no mountain high enough) ah ha
Gm7
(Ain't no valley low enough) ooh,
Fm7
(Ain't no river wide enough) ah oh,
E♭maj7 Csus4 C
(To keep me from you).
A♭maj7
(Ain't no mountain high enough)
Gm7
(Ain't no valley low enough) say it again,
Fm7
(Ain't no river wide enough) hey,
E♭maj7 Csus4 C
(To keep me from you.)
A♭maj7 E♭maj7
Ain't no mountain high enough,
A♭maj7 E♭maj7 Csus4 C
Nothing can keep me, keep me from you.___

Instrumental | D♭11 | G♭maj7 | D♭11 | G♭maj7 B♭m7 E♭7 ||

Chorus 2

D♭11
(Ain't no mountain high enough) ah oh,
G♭maj7
(Ain't no valley low enough) one more time,
D♭11
(Ain't no river wide enough) say it again,
G♭maj7 B♭m7 E♭7
(To keep me from you).___
D♭11 G♭maj7
Ain't no mountain high enough
D♭11 G♭maj7 B♭m7 E♭7
Nothing can keep me, keep me from you.___

| D♭11 | G♭maj7 | D♭11 | G♭maj7 B♭m7 E♭7 || *Ad lib. to fade*

Bad Day

Words & Music by Daniel Powter

D5 (fr3) Gsus2 (fr3) Asus2 (fr3) D/A G5/A Bm D/A G

D/F♯ Em7 A D Gsus2* Asus4* B♭aug E/G♯

Capo first fret

Intro | D5 | Gsus2 | Asus4 | D/A G5/A ||

```
           D5                Gsus2                   Asus4  D/A  G5/A
*Verse 1*    Where is the moment we needed the most?
           D5                   Gsus2                    Asus4  D/A  G5/A
             You kick up the leaves and the magic is lost.
           Bm                 D/A*              G
             They tell me your blue skies fade to grey,
                             D/F♯                Em7
           They tell me your passion's gone a - way
                                      A
           And I don't need no carryin' on.

           D                    G                  A    G
*Verse 2*    You stand in the line just to hit a new low,
           D                  G                           A
             You're faking a smile with the coffee to go.
           Bm                 D/A*                G
             They tell me your life's been way off line,
                           D/F♯                 Em7
           You're falling to pieces every time
                                      A
           And I don't need no carryin' on.
```

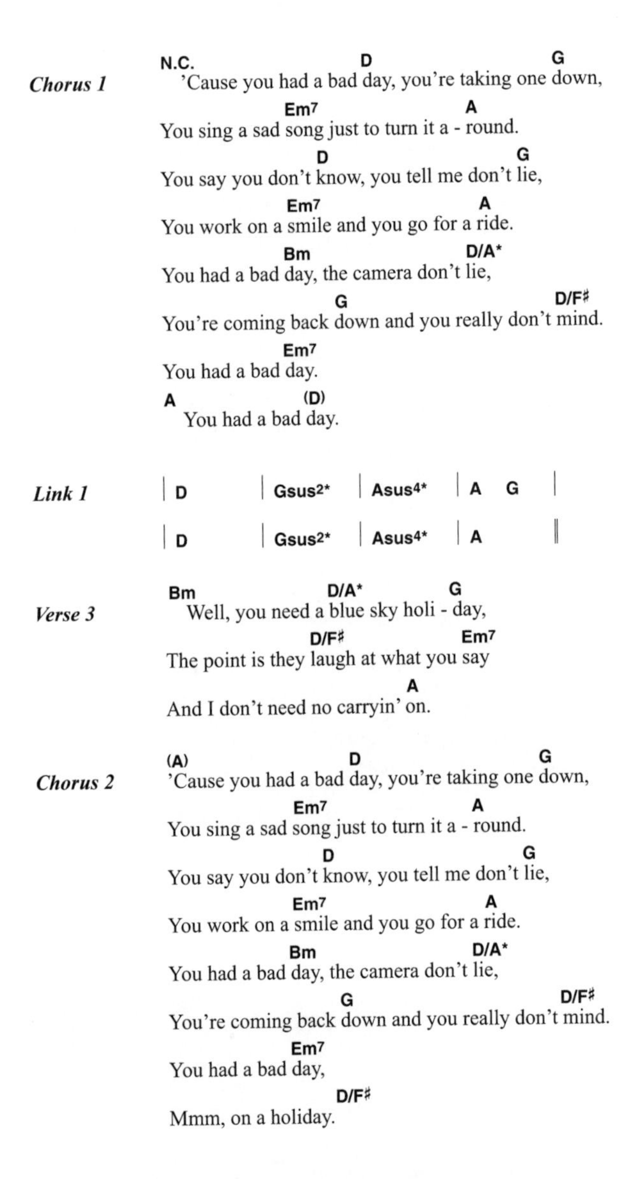
Chorus 1
N.C. D G
'Cause you had a bad day, you're taking one down,
Em7 A
You sing a sad song just to turn it a - round.
D G
You say you don't know, you tell me don't lie,
Em7 A
You work on a smile and you go for a ride.
Bm D/A*
You had a bad day, the camera don't lie,
G D/F♯
You're coming back down and you really don't mind.
Em7
You had a bad day.
A (D)
You had a bad day.
Link 1
| D | Gsus2* | Asus4* | A G |
| D | Gsus2* | Asus4* | A ||
Verse 3
Bm D/A* G
Well, you need a blue sky holi - day,
D/F♯ Em7
The point is they laugh at what you say
A
And I don't need no carryin' on.
Chorus 2
(A) D G
'Cause you had a bad day, you're taking one down,
Em7 A
You sing a sad song just to turn it a - round.
D G
You say you don't know, you tell me don't lie,
Em7 A
You work on a smile and you go for a ride.
Bm D/A*
You had a bad day, the camera don't lie,
G D/F♯
You're coming back down and you really don't mind.
Em7
You had a bad day,
D/F♯
Mmm, on a holiday.

Bridge

F
Sometimes the system goes on the blink
B♭
And the whole thing it turns out wrong.
F
You might not make it back and you know
B♭
That you could be well oh, that strong
Asus4* A
And I'm not wrong, yeah.__

Verse 4

D G A
So where was the passion when you need it the most?
D G A
Oh, you and I, you kick up the leaves and the magic is lost.

Chorus 3

(A) D G
'Cause you had a bad day, you're taking one down,
Em7 A
You sing a sad song just to turn it a - round.
D G
You say you don't know, you tell me don't lie,
Em7 A
You work on a smile and you go for a ride.
Bm B♭aug
You had a bad day, you see what you're like
D/A* E/G♯
And how does it feel a one more time?
G
You had a bad day.
Asus4* (D)
You had a bad day.

Outro

D G Em7 A D
Had a bad day.
𝄆 G Em7 A D 𝄇 *Repeat to fade*
Had a bad day.

Baby, Come Back

Words & Music by Eddy Grant

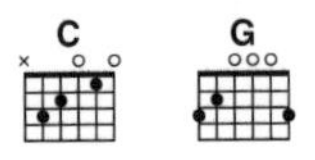

Intro | C G | C G | C G | C G | C G | C G ||

Chorus 1

```
     C   G
Come back
           C    G
Baby, come back
           C    G
Baby, come back
           C    G
Baby, come back
```

Verse 1

```
G
This is the first time until today

That you have run away

I'm asking you for the first time

Lover you know that it's fair

Hey, hey, hey
```

Chorus 2

```
     C   G
Come back
           C    G
Baby, come back
           C    G
Baby, come back
           C    G
Baby, come back
```

Verse 2

G
There ain't no use in you crying

'Cause I'm more hurt than you, yeah

I shouldn't caught, been a-flirting

But now my love is a-true, yeah

Ooh yeah, ooh yeah

Ooh yeah

Chorus 3

C G
Come back

C G
Baby, come back

C G
Baby, come back

C G
Baby, come back

Verse 3

G
Come back baby don't you leave me

Baby, baby, please don't go

Oh, won't you give me a second chance

Baby, I love you so

Oh, oh yeah

Oh yeah

Chorus 4

C G
𝄆 Come back

C G
Baby, come back

C G
Baby, come back

C G
Baby, come back 𝄇 *Repeat ad lib. to fade*

Back For Good

Words & Music by Gary Barlow

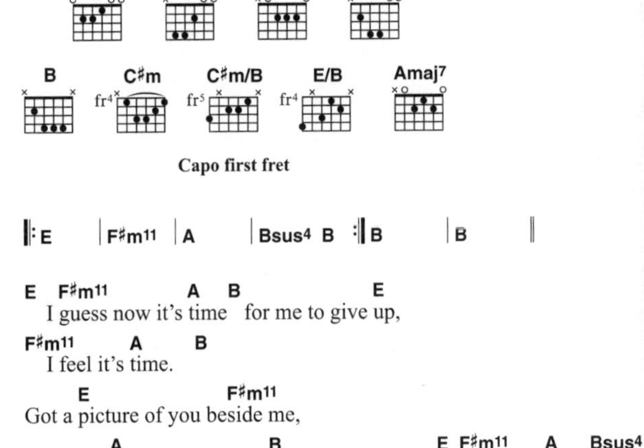

Capo first fret

Intro ‖: E | F♯m11 | A | Bsus4 B :‖ B | B ‖

Verse 1

E F♯m11 A B E
I guess now it's time for me to give up,
F♯m11 A B
I feel it's time.
E F♯m11
Got a picture of you beside me,
A B E F♯m11 A Bsus4
Got your lipstick mark still on your coffee cup, oh, yeah.
B E F♯m11
Got a fist of pure emotion,
A B
Got a head of shattered dreams,
C♯m C♯m/B E/B A Bsus4 B
Gotta leave it, gotta leave it all behind now.

Chorus 1

E F♯m11 A
Whatever I said, whatever I did I didn't mean it,
B E F♯m11 A Bsus4 B
I just want you back for good.
E F♯m11 A
Whenever I'm wrong just tell me the song and I'll sing it,
B E F♯m11
You'll be right and understood.
A Bsus4 B
I want you back for good.

Verse 2

E F♯m11 A B E
Unaware but underlined I figured out the story.
F♯m11 A B
It wasn't good.
E F♯m11 A B
But in a corner of my mind
E
I celebrated glory,
F♯m11 A Bsus4 B
But that was not to be.
E F♯m11 A B
In the twist of separation you excelled at being free,
C♯m C♯m/B E/B A Bsus4 B
Can't you find a little room inside for me?

Chorus 2

E F♯m11 A
Whatever I said, whatever I did I didn't mean it,
B E F♯m11
I just want you back for good.
(F♯m11) A Bsus4 B
You see I want you back for good.
E F♯m11 A
Whenever I'm wrong just tell me the song and I'll sing it,
B E F♯m11
You'll be right and understood.
A Bsus4 B
I want you back for good.

Middle

Amaj7 E
And we'll be together,
Amaj7 E
This time it's forever.
Amaj7 E
We'll be fighting and forever we will be
C♯m C♯m/B
So complete in our love.
Amaj7 E B Bsus4 B
We will never be uncovered again.

Chorus 3

As Chorus 1 *(w/ad lib. vocals)*

Chorus 4

As Chorus 1 *(w/ad lib. vocals)*

Outro

E F♯m11 A Bsus4 B
Oh, yeah
E F♯m11 A Bsus4 B E
I guess now it's time that you came back for good.

Because Of You

Words & Music by Kelly Clarkson, Ben Moody & David Hodges

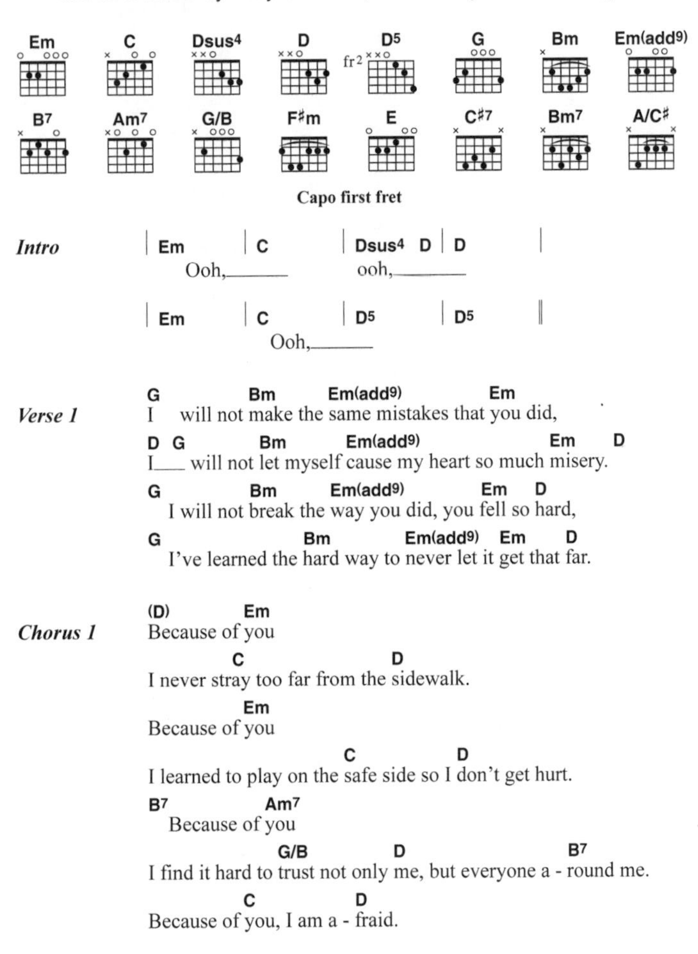

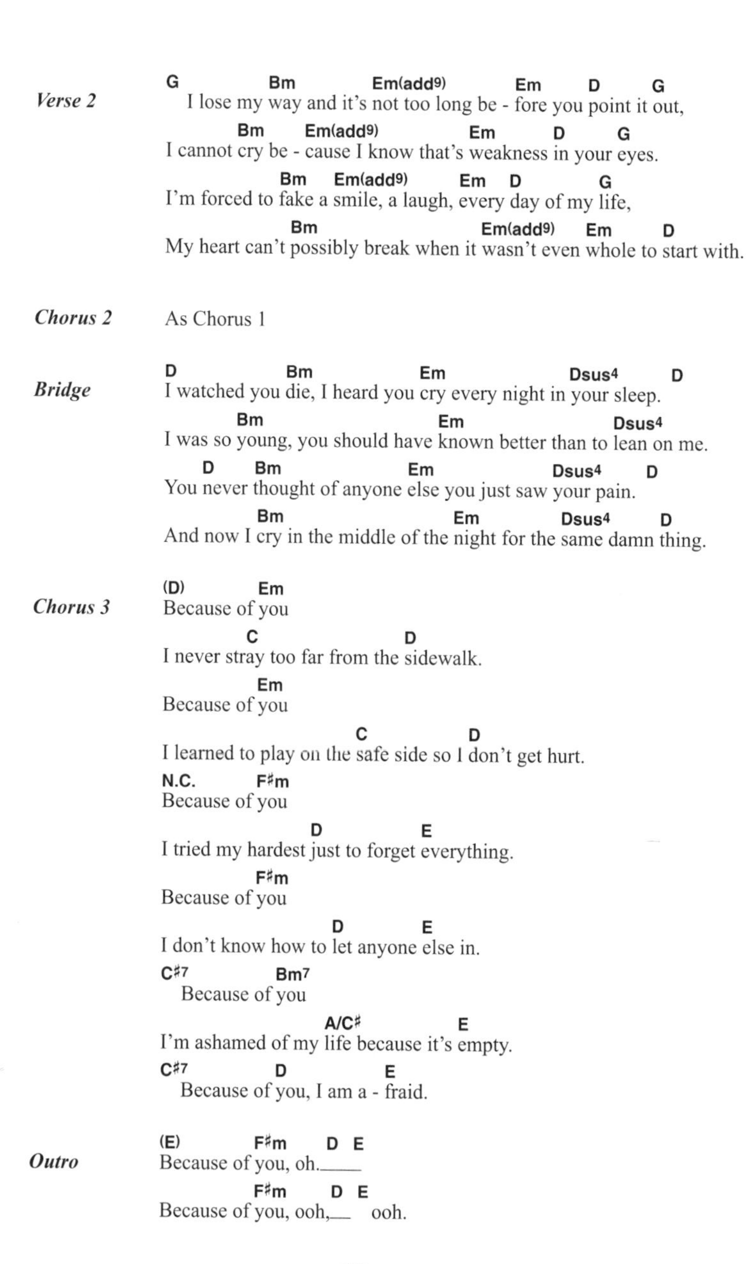
Verse 2
G Bm Em(add9) Em D G
I lose my way and it's not too long be - fore you point it out,
Bm Em(add9) Em D G
I cannot cry be - cause I know that's weakness in your eyes.
Bm Em(add9) Em D G
I'm forced to fake a smile, a laugh, every day of my life,
Bm Em(add9) Em D
My heart can't possibly break when it wasn't even whole to start with.
Chorus 2
As Chorus 1
Bridge
D Bm Em Dsus4 D
I watched you die, I heard you cry every night in your sleep.
Bm Em Dsus4
I was so young, you should have known better than to lean on me.
D Bm Em Dsus4 D
You never thought of anyone else you just saw your pain.
Bm Em Dsus4 D
And now I cry in the middle of the night for the same damn thing.
Chorus 3
(D) Em
Because of you
C D
I never stray too far from the sidewalk.
Em
Because of you
C D
I learned to play on the safe side so I don't get hurt.
N.C. F♯m
Because of you
D E
I tried my hardest just to forget everything.
F♯m
Because of you
D E
I don't know how to let anyone else in.
C♯7 Bm7
Because of you
A/C♯ E
I'm ashamed of my life because it's empty.
C♯7 D E
Because of you, I am a - fraid.
Outro
(E) F♯m D E
Because of you, oh.
F♯m D E
Because of you, ooh, ooh.

Big Love

Words & Music By Lindsey Buckingham

Dm C B♭ Am Gm (fr3)

To match original recording, tune guitar slightly sharp

Intro

```
| Dm    | C     | B♭    | Am    |
| Dm    | C     | B♭    | Am    ||
```

Verse 1

```
                    Dm
Looking out for love,
C                  B♭   Am
   In the night so still,
         Dm          C
Oh, I'll build you a kingdom
       B♭          Am
In that house on the hill.
```

Chorus 1

```
                   Gm Am | Dm     | Gm Am | Dm     |
Looking out for love,
            Gm Am | Dm     | Gm Am | Dm     |
Big, big love.
```

Verse 2

```
                        Dm
You said that you love me,
C                        B♭     Am
   And that you always will,
          Dm           C
Oh, you begged me to keep you
       B♭          Am
In that house on the hill.
```

Chorus 2 As Verse 1

Guitar solo

Gm Am	Dm	Gm Am	Dm
Gm Am	Dm	Gm Am	Dm
Dm	C	B♭	Am
Dm	C	B♭	Am	

Bridge

```
Dm         C                    B♭ Am
I wake up    alone with it all,
         Dm       C             B♭ Am
I wake up, but only to fall.
```

Chorus 3 As Chorus 1

Chorus 4 As Chorus 1

Outro

||: Gm Am | Dm | Gm Am | Dm |
| Gm Am | Dm | Gm Am | Dm :|| *Repeat ad lib. to fade*

Black Night

Words & Music by Ritchie Blackmore, Ian Gillan, Roger Glover, Jon Lord & Ian Paice

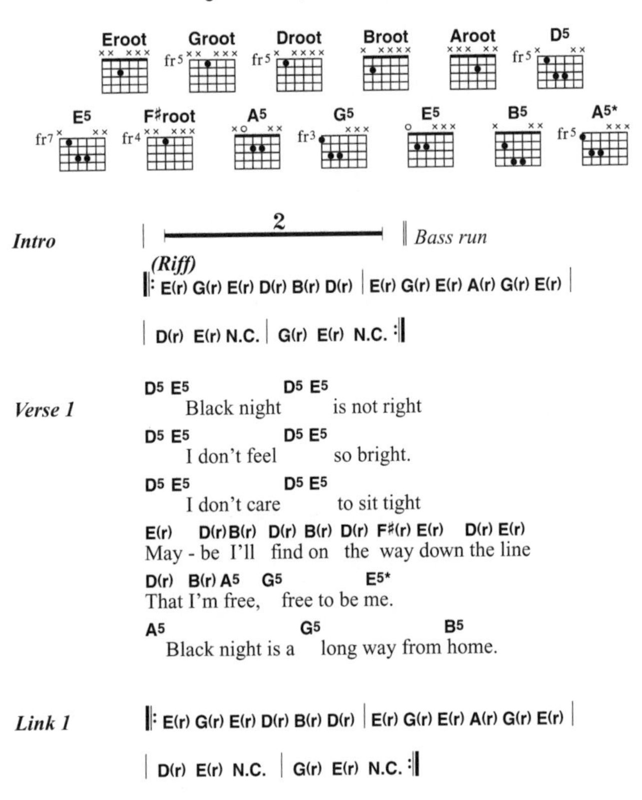

Verse 2

```
D5 E5           D5 E5
    I don't need     a dark tree
D5 E5           D5 E5
    I don't want     a rough sea,
D5 E5           D5 E5
    I can't feel,    I can't see
E(r)   D(r)B(r) D(r) B(r) D(r) F♯(r) E(r)   D(r) E(r)
May - be  I'll  find on  the  way down the line
D(r)  B(r) A5   G5           E5*
That I'm free,   free to be me
A5                  G5                B5
  Black night is a   long way from home.
```

Instrumental 1 𝄆 D5 E5 | D5 E5 𝄇 *Play 6 times*

Link 2 | E(r) D(r) B(r) D(r) B(r) D(r) | F♯(r) E(r) D(r) E(r) D(r) B(r) ‖

Instrumental 2 𝄆 G5 A5* | G5 A5* 𝄇 *Play 6 times*

Link 3 As Link 1

Verse 3

```
D5 E5           D5 E5
    Black night,     black night
D5 E5           D5 E5
    I don't need,     black night,
D5 E5           D5 E5
    I can't see,    dark light
E(r)   D(r)B(r) D(r) B(r) D(r) F♯(r) E(r)   D(r) E(r)
May - be  I'll  find on  the  way down the line
D(r)  B(r) A5   G5           E5*
That I'm free,   free to be me
A5                  G5                B5
  Black night is a   long way from home.
```

Outro 𝄆 D5 E5 | D5 E5 𝄇 *Repeat to fade*

Born To Die

Words & Music by Elizabeth Grant & Justin Parker

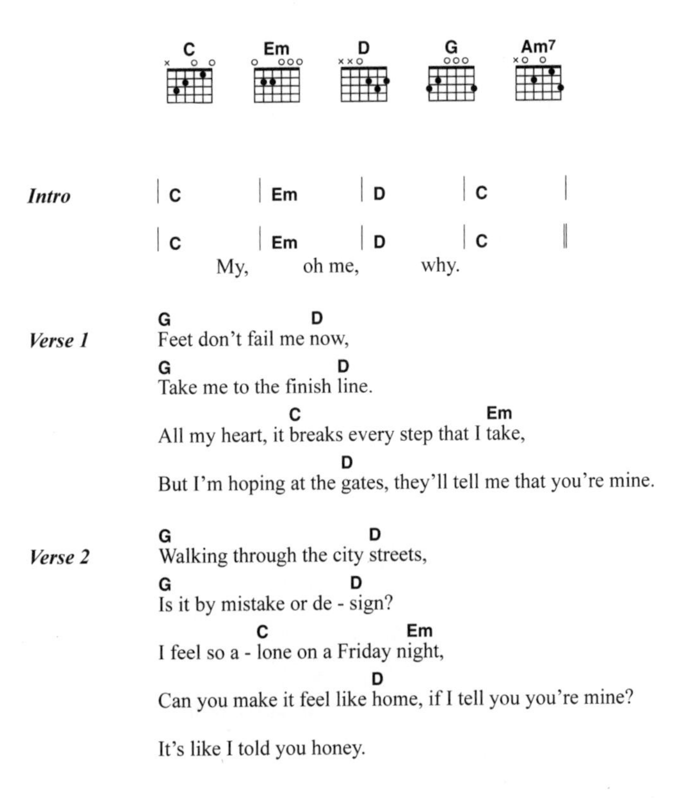

Intro

| C | Em | D | C |

| C | Em | D | C ||

My, oh me, why.

Verse 1

G D
Feet don't fail me now,
G D
Take me to the finish line.
C Em
All my heart, it breaks every step that I take,
D
But I'm hoping at the gates, they'll tell me that you're mine.

Verse 2

G D
Walking through the city streets,
G D
Is it by mistake or de - sign?
C Em
I feel so a - lone on a Friday night,
D
Can you make it feel like home, if I tell you you're mine?

It's like I told you honey.

```
              C         Em                             D
Pre-chorus 1    Don't make me sad, don't make me cry,
                                     C
              Sometimes life is not e - nough and the road gets tough,

              I don't know why.
                                  Em                  D
              Keep making me laugh, let's go get high.
                                         C
              The road is long, we carry on,

              Try to have fun in the meantime.

              C                                       Em
Chorus 1        Come and take a walk on the wild side,
                                                    D
              Let me kiss you hard in the pouring rain.
                                    C
              You like your girls in - sane.
                                Em                     D
              Choose your last words, this is the last time,
                                C
              'Cause you and I, we were born to die.

              G                 D
Verse 3       Lost but now I am found,
              G                         D
              I can see that once I was blind.
                            C                Em
              I was so con - fused as a little child,
                                           C
              Trying to take what I could get, scared that I couldn't find

              All the answers, honey.

Pre-chorus 2  As Pre-chorus 1

Chorus 2      As Chorus 1
```

Bridge

```
C  Em                   D    C
      We were born to die.
                  Em
We were born to die.
Am7
   Come and take a walk on the wild side,
Em                                   D
   Let me kiss you hard in the pouring rain.

You like your girls insane.
```

Pre-chorus 3 As Pre-chorus 1

Chorus 3 As Chorus 1

Outro

```
||: C     | Em    | D     | C     :||
|   C     | Em    | D     ||
```

Enola Gay

Words & Music by Andy McCluskey

F Dm B♭ C

Intro

| F | F | Dm | Dm |
| B♭ | B♭ | C | C |

Verse 1

```
   F
E - nola Gay,
                                    Dm
You should have stayed at home yesterday.
         B♭
Oh, it can't describe
                         C
The feeling and the way you lied.
```

Verse 2

```
(C)    F
These games you play,
                             Dm
They're gonna end it all in tears someday.
                B♭
Oh, oh, E - nola Gay,
                           C
It shouldn't ever have to end this way.
```

Instrumental 1

| F | F | Dm | Dm |
| B♭ | B♭ | C | C |

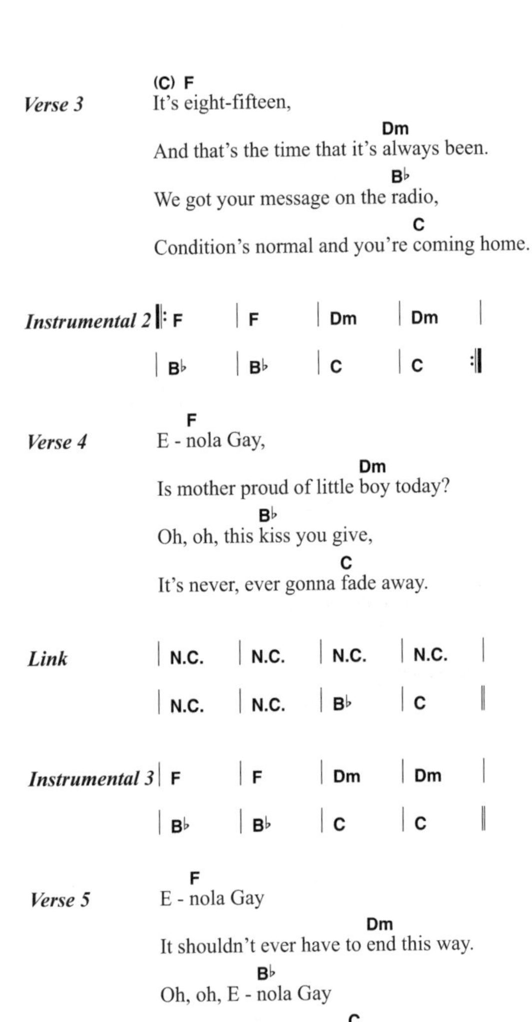

Verse 3

(C) F
It's eight-fifteen,
Dm
And that's the time that it's always been.
B♭
We got your message on the radio,
C
Condition's normal and you're coming home.

Instrumental 2

‖: F | F | Dm | Dm |
| B♭ | B♭ | C | C :‖

Verse 4

F
E - nola Gay,
Dm
Is mother proud of little boy today?
B♭
Oh, oh, this kiss you give,
C
It's never, ever gonna fade away.

Link

| N.C. | N.C. | N.C. | N.C. |
| N.C. | N.C. | B♭ | C ‖

Instrumental 3

| F | F | Dm | Dm |
| B♭ | B♭ | C | C ‖

Verse 5

F
E - nola Gay
Dm
It shouldn't ever have to end this way.
B♭
Oh, oh, E - nola Gay
C
It should've faded our dreams away.

Verse 6

(C) F
It's eight-fifteen,

Dm
And that's the time that it's always been.

B♭
We got your message on the radio,

C
Condition's normal and you're coming home.

Verse 7

F
E - nola Gay,

Dm
Is mother proud of little boy today?

B♭
Oh, oh, this kiss you give,

C F
It's never, ever gonna fade away.___

Bright Eyes

Words & Music by Mike Batt

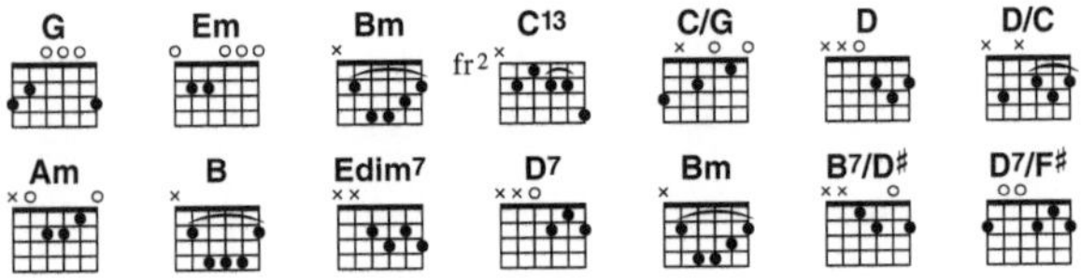

G Em Bm C13 C/G D D/C

Am B Edim7 D7 Bm B7/D♯ D7/F♯

Intro

G	G	Em	Em
Bm	Bm	C13	C13
G	G	G	G	

Verse 1

```
G                C/G   G
Is it a kind of dream___
Em                    C     G
Floating out on the tide,___
D              D/C      G              C
Following the river of death down - stream,
     Am    D           Dsus4  D
Oh, is it a dream?
             G                     C/G G
There's a fog along the ho  -  ri  -  zon,
  Em                     C    G
A strange glow in the sky.___
      D          D/C              G          C
And nobody seems to know where it goes
                           B
And what does it mean?
Edim7  D    D7     G
Oh,___      is it a dream?
```

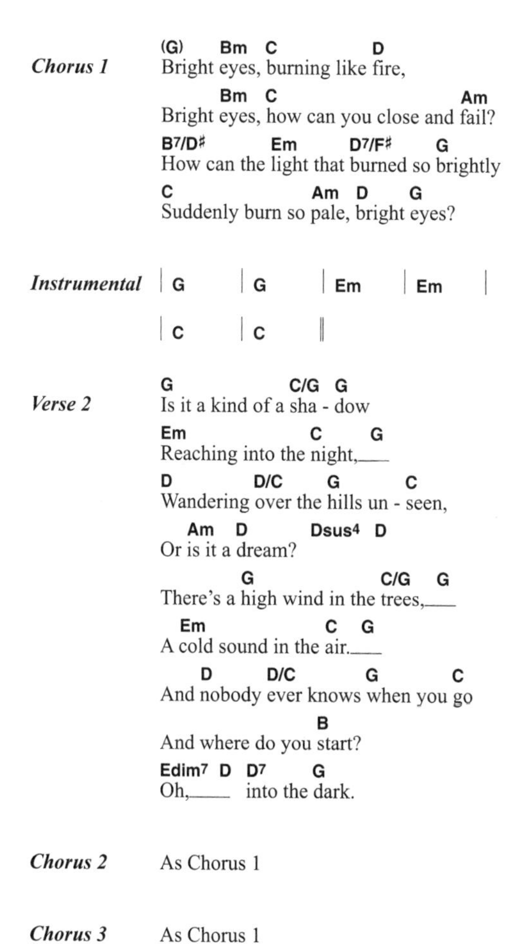

Chorus 1

(G) Bm C D
Bright eyes, burning like fire,

Bm C Am
Bright eyes, how can you close and fail?

B7/D♯ Em D7/F♯ G
How can the light that burned so brightly

C Am D G
Suddenly burn so pale, bright eyes?

Instrumental

| G | G | Em | Em |
| C | C ||

Verse 2

G C/G G
Is it a kind of a sha - dow

Em C G
Reaching into the night,___

D D/C G C
Wandering over the hills un - seen,

Am D Dsus4 D
Or is it a dream?

G C/G G
There's a high wind in the trees,___

Em C G
A cold sound in the air.___

D D/C G C
And nobody ever knows when you go

B
And where do you start?

Edim7 D D7 G
Oh,___ into the dark.

Chorus 2 As Chorus 1

Chorus 3 As Chorus 1

Can't Get You Out Of My Head

Words & Music by Cathy Dennis & Rob Davis

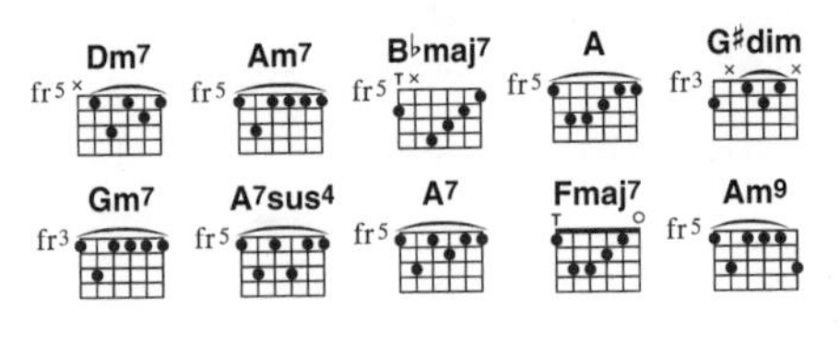

Intro ‖: Dm7 | Am7 | Dm7 | Am7 :‖

Link 1

Dm7
La la la, la la la la la,
Am7
La la la, la la la la la.
Dm7
La la la, la la la la la,
Am7
La la la, la la la la la.

Chorus 1

Dm7
I just can't get you out of my head,
Am7
Boy your loving is all I think about.
Dm7
I just can't get you out of my head,
Am7
Boy it's more than I dare to think about.

Link 2

Dm7
La la la, la la la la la,
Am7
La la la, la la la la la.

Chorus 2

Dm7
I just can't get you out of my head,
Am7
Boy, your loving is all I think about.

cont.

```
        Dm7
I just can't get you out of my head,
           Am7
Boy, it's more than I dare to think about.
```

Verse 1

```
B♭maj7 A
Every  night,
G♯dim  A
Every  day,
Gm7                         A7sus4
Just to be there in your arms,
          Dm7          Am7
Won't you stay?__________
          Dm7          Am7
Won't you     lay,__________
          B♭maj7                A7
Stay for - ever and ever and ever and ever.
```

Link 3 As Link 1

Chorus 3 As Chorus 2

Verse 2

```
B♭maj7   A    G♯dim    A
There's a dark secret in    me,
Gm7                                A7sus4
Don't leave me locked in your heart.
         Dm7    Am7
Set me free,____
          Dm7             Am7
Feel the     need____ in  me,
         Dm7       Fmaj7 Am9
Set me free,____
          B♭maj7              N.C.      A7
Stay for - ever and ever and ever and ever.
```

Link 4 As Link 1

Outro

```
          Dm7
𝄆 I just can't get you out of my head,
 Am7
(La la la, la la la la la.) 𝄇  Repeat to fade
```

Cry

Words & Music by Kevin Godley & Lol Creme

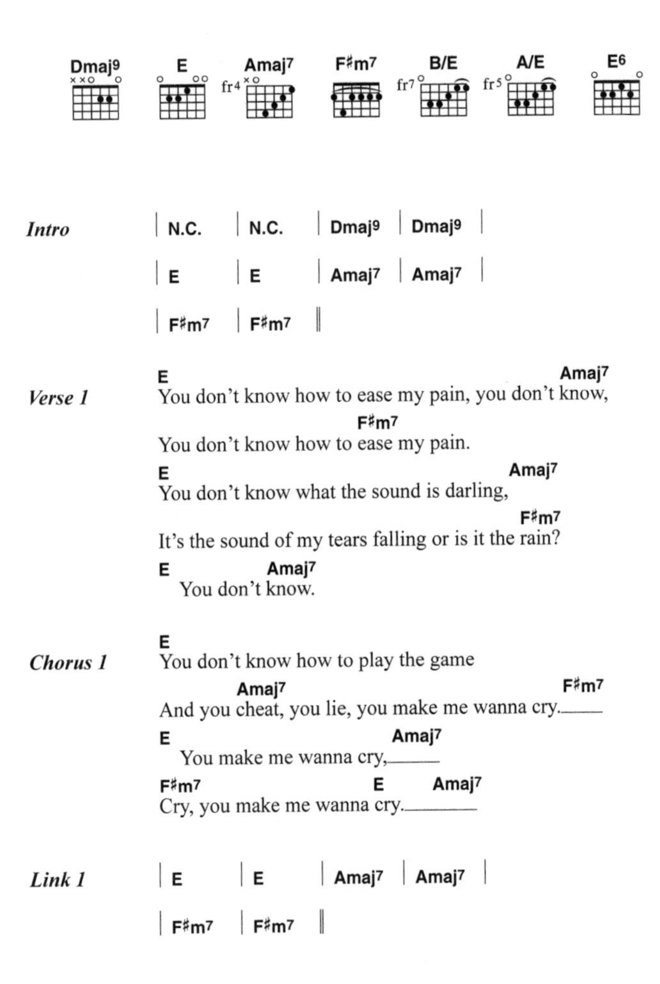

Intro

| N.C. | N.C. | Dmaj9 | Dmaj9 |

| E | E | Amaj7 | Amaj7 |

| F♯m7 | F♯m7 ||

Verse 1

E   Amaj7
You don't know how to ease my pain, you don't know,
                                        F♯m7
You don't know how to ease my pain.
E   Amaj7
You don't know what the sound is darling,
                                                                F♯m7
It's the sound of my tears falling or is it the rain?
E   Amaj7
  You don't know.

Chorus 1

E
You don't know how to play the game
              Amaj7   F♯m7
And you cheat, you lie, you make me wanna cry._____
E   Amaj7
  You make me wanna cry,_____
F♯m7   E   Amaj7
Cry, you make me wanna cry._____

Link 1

| E | E | Amaj7 | Amaj7 |

| F♯m7 | F♯m7 ||

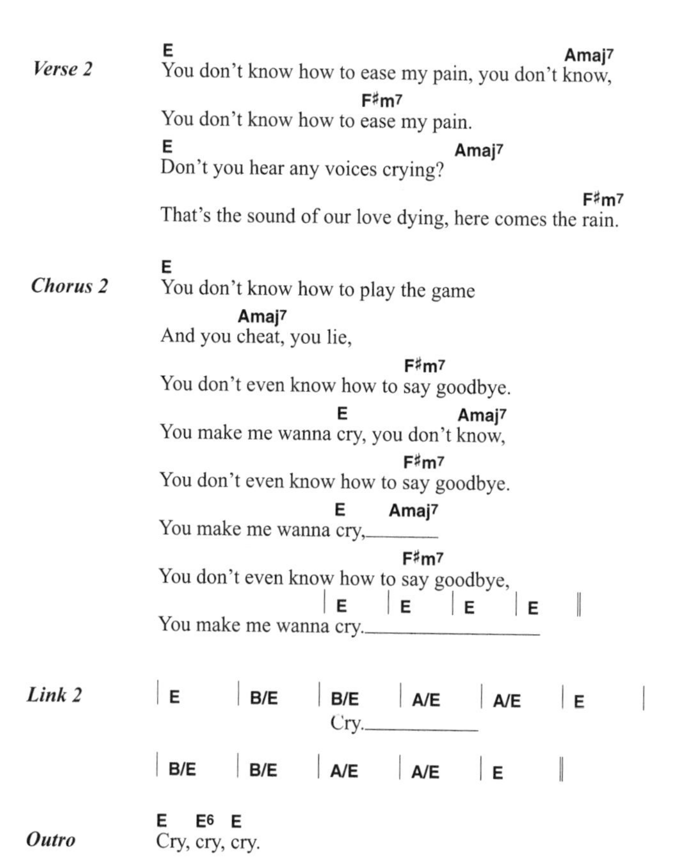

```
             E                                              Amaj7
Verse 2      You don't know how to ease my pain, you don't know,
                                   F#m7
             You don't know how to ease my pain.
             E                             Amaj7
             Don't you hear any voices crying?
                                                              F#m7
             That's the sound of our love dying, here comes the rain.

             E
Chorus 2     You don't know how to play the game
                     Amaj7
             And you cheat, you lie,
                                           F#m7
             You don't even know how to say goodbye.
                                   E            Amaj7
             You make me wanna cry, you don't know,
                                           F#m7
             You don't even know how to say goodbye.
                                   E       Amaj7
             You make me wanna cry,______
                                           F#m7
             You don't even know how to say goodbye,
                                 | E    | E    | E    | E    ||
             You make me wanna cry.______________________

Link 2       | E     | B/E   | B/E   | A/E   | A/E   | E     |
                               Cry.________
             | B/E   | B/E   | A/E   | A/E   | E     ||

             E   E6  E
Outro        Cry, cry, cry.
```

Dancing In The Street

Words & Music by Marvin Gaye, William Stevenson & Ivy Hunter

Bm7/E   E   A   G♯7 (fr4)   C♯m (fr4)   F♯m   B7sus4 (fr2)   B7♭9

Intro | Bm7/E E | Bm7/E E | Bm7/E E | Bm7/E E ||

Verse 1

```
Bm7/E  E    Bm7/E      E
Calling out around the world
             Bm7/E      E               Bm7/E   E
Are you ready for a brand new beat?
Bm7/E       E              Bm7/E   E
Summer's here and the time is   right
      Bm7/E  E       Bm7/E
For dancing in the street.
            E                        Bm7/E   E  Bm7/E  E
They're dancing down in Chicago, ____
             Bm7/E    E
Down in New Orleans,
Bm7/E    E            Bm7/E   E
   In      New York City.
```

Pre-chorus 1

```
Bm7/E     E        A
All   we need is music, sweet music,

There'll be music everywhere,
                  Bm7/E    E                 Bm7/E   E
There'll be swingers swaying and records playing,
Bm7/E     E       Bm7/E    E
Dancing in the street,    oh.
```

Chorus 1

```
G♯7
   It doesn't matter what you wear
         C♯m
Just as long as you are there,
              F♯m
So come on, every guy grab a girl,
B7sus4          B7♭9
Everywhere around the world.
```

Verse 2

Bm7/E E
They'll be dancing,

Bm7/E E Bm7/E E Bm7/E E
They're dancing in the street.

Bm7/E E Bm7/E E
This is an invi - tation across the nation,

Bm7/E E Bm7/E E
A chance for folks to meet.

Bm7/E E Bm7/E E
There'll be laughter, singing, and music swinging,

Bm7/E E Bm7/E
Dancing in the street.

E Bm7/E E Bm7/E
Philadephia, P.A., (dancing in the street),

E Bm7/E E
Baltimore and D.C. now, (dancing in the street),

Bm7/E E Bm7/E E
Can't forget the Motorcity (dancing in the street).

Pre-chorus 2 As Pre-chorus 1

Chorus 2 As Chorus 1

Coda

Bm7/E E Bm7/E E Bm7/E E
They're dancing, they're dancing in the street.

Bm7/E E Bm7/E E Bm7/E
Way down in L.A. every day

E Bm7/E E
They're dancing in the street.

Bm7/E E Bm7/E E Bm7/E
Let's form a big strong line, get in time:

E Bm7/E E
We're dancing in the street.

Bm7/E E Bm7/E E
Across the ocean blue, me and you.

Fade out

The Dark End Of The Street

Words & Music by Dan Penn & Chips Moman

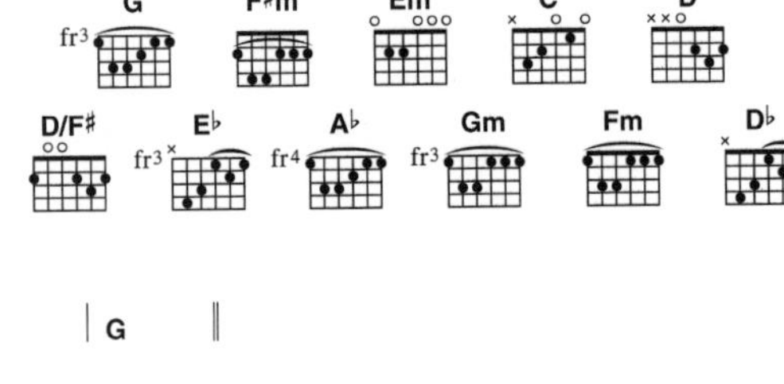

Intro | G ‖

Verse 1

N.C. G F♯m Em
At the dark end of the street,
G F♯m Em
That's where we always meet.
G C D G
Hiding in shadows where we don't be - long,
C D G
Living in darkness to hide our wrong.
C G C D G
You and me at the dark end of the street,
C G D
You and me.

Verse 2

(D) G F♯m Em
I know time is gonna take its toll,
G F♯m Em
We have to pay for the love we stole.
G C D G
It's a sin and we know it's wrong,
C D G
Oh, but our love keeps coming on strong.
C G C D G
Steal a - way to the dark end of the street.
C G D
Mmm.___

Bridge

```
(D)                  G
They're gonna find us,
                     F♯m   D/F♯
They're gonna find us,
                       Em                G
They're gonna find us, Lord, some day,
C          G          C          D       G
   You and me at the dark end    of the street
C          G
   You and me.
```

Verse 3

```
E♭                    A♭        Gm            Fm
   And when the daylight hours roll a - round,
           A♭            Gm          Fm
And by chance we're both down - town.
                   A♭   D♭        E♭  A♭
If we should meet just walk on  by,
     D♭       E♭                A♭
Oh, darling,     please don't cry.
D♭                   A♭           D♭           E♭        A♭
   Tonight, we'll meet at the dark end      of the street.
E♭                A♭
Mmm, mmm.
```

Do You Realize??

Words & Music by Wayne Coyne, Steven Drozd,
Michael Ivins & Dave Fridmann

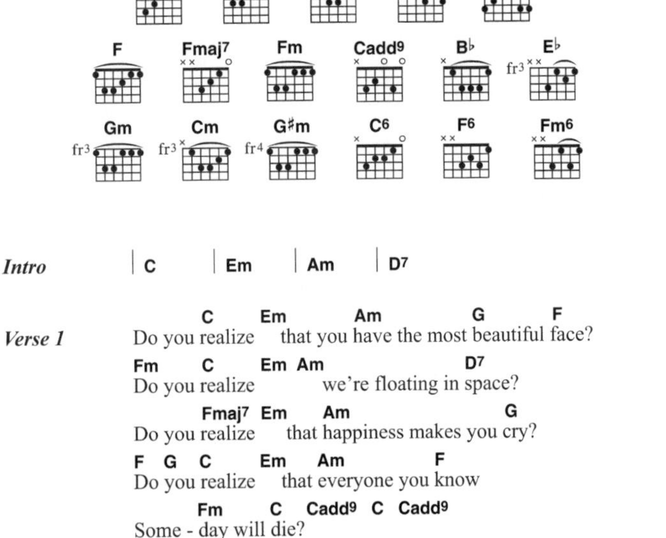

Intro | C | Em | Am | D7

Verse 1

```
          C      Em          Am              G        F
Do you realize    that you have the most beautiful face?
Fm        C      Em  Am                D7
Do you realize          we're floating in space?
          Fmaj7  Em     Am                       G
Do you realize    that happiness makes you cry?
F  G   C         Em     Am              F
Do you realize    that everyone you know
         Fm        C    Cadd9  C   Cadd9
Some - day will die?
         F                 Am                 G
And in - stead of saying all of your good - byes, let them know…
```

Bridge 1

```
      C          F
You realize that life goes fast,
     C                  G
It's hard to make the good things last.
      C                Em
You realize the sun doesn't go down,
     G              F               G              C       Fm
It's just an illusion caused by the world spinning round.
```

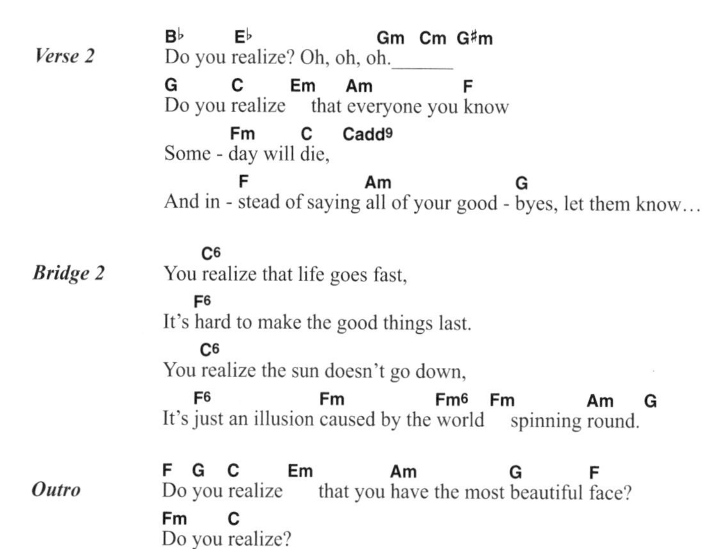
Verse 2
B♭ E♭ Gm Cm G♯m
Do you realize? Oh, oh, oh.______
G C Em Am F
Do you realize that everyone you know
Fm C Cadd9
Some - day will die,
F Am G
And in - stead of saying all of your good - byes, let them know…
Bridge 2
C6
You realize that life goes fast,
F6
It's hard to make the good things last.
C6
You realize the sun doesn't go down,
F6 Fm Fm6 Fm Am G
It's just an illusion caused by the world spinning round.
Outro
F G C Em Am G F
Do you realize that you have the most beautiful face?
Fm C
Do you realize?

Dream Lover

Words & Music by Bobby Darin

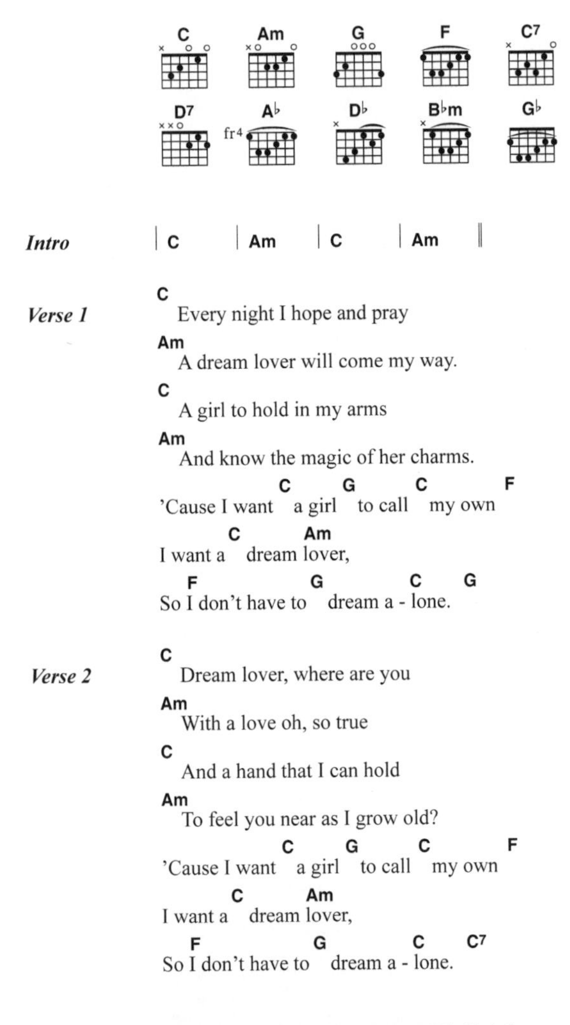

Intro | C | Am | C | Am ||

Verse 1

C
Every night I hope and pray
Am
A dream lover will come my way.
C
A girl to hold in my arms
Am
And know the magic of her charms.
C G C F
'Cause I want a girl to call my own
C Am
I want a dream lover,
F G C G
So I don't have to dream a - lone.

Verse 2

C
Dream lover, where are you
Am
With a love oh, so true
C
And a hand that I can hold
Am
To feel you near as I grow old?
C G C F
'Cause I want a girl to call my own
C Am
I want a dream lover,
F G C C7
So I don't have to dream a - lone.

Bridge

```
F
  Some day, I don't know how,
C
  I hope she'll hear my plea.
D7
  Some way, I don't know how,
G
  She'll bring her love to me.
```

Verse 3

```
C
  Dream lover until then
Am
  I'll go to sleep and dream again.
C
  That's the only thing to do
Am
  Till all my lover's dreams come true.
             C      G       C         F
'Cause I want  a girl  to call  my own
        C       Am
I want a  dream lover,
  F              G          C     A♭
So I don't have to  dream a - lone.
```

Verse 4

```
D♭
  Dream lover until then
B♭m
  I'll go to sleep and dream again.
D♭
  That's the only thing to do
B♭m
  Till all my lover's dreams come true.
             D♭     A♭       D♭       G♭
'Cause I want  a girl  to call  my own
        D♭      B♭m
I want a  dream lover,
  G♭             A♭         D♭
So I don't have to  dream a - lone.
```

Outro

```
B♭m                     D♭
  Please don't make me dream alone.
B♭m                          D♭
  I beg you, don't make me dream alone.
B♭m                 D♭            B♭m
  No, I don't wanna dream alone.____      To fade
```

Easy

Words & Music by Lionel Richie

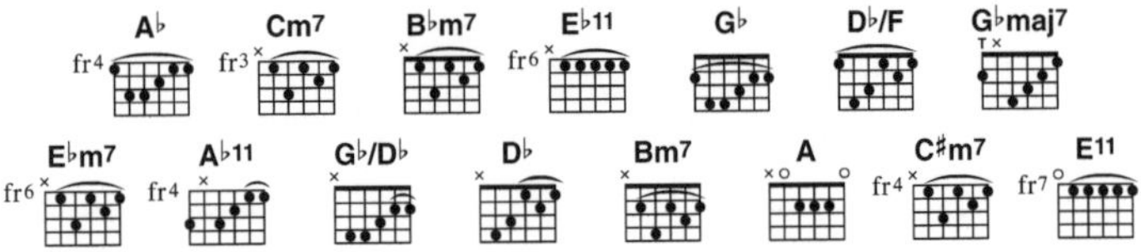

A♭ Cm7 B♭m7 E♭11 G♭ D♭/F G♭maj7
E♭m7 A♭11 G♭/D♭ D♭ Bm7 A C♯m7 E11

Intro | A♭ | Cm7 | B♭m7 | E♭11 |
| A♭ | Cm7 | B♭m7 | B♭m7 ||

Verse 1
A♭ Cm7 B♭m7 E♭11
Know it sounds funny, but I just can't stand the pain,
A♭ Cm7 B♭m7 E♭11
Girl, I'm leaving you tomor - row.
A♭ Cm7 B♭m7 E♭11
Seems to me girl you know I've done all I can,
A♭ Cm7 B♭m7 E♭11
You see I begged, stole and I borrowed, yeah.

Chorus 1
(E♭11) A♭ Cm7 B♭m7
Ooh, that's why I'm ea - sy,
E♭11 A♭ Cm7 B♭m7
I'm easy like Sunday morn - ing.
E♭11 A♭ Cm7 B♭m7
That's why I'm ea - sy,________
E♭11 G♭ D♭/F E♭11 A♭
I'm easy like Sunday morn - ing.

Verse 2
A♭ Cm7 B♭m7 E♭11
Why in the world would anybody put chains on me?
A♭ Cm7 B♭m7 E♭11
I've paid my dues to make it.
A♭ Cm7 B♭m7 E♭11
Everybody wants me to be what they want me to be,
A♭ Cm7 B♭m7 E♭11
I'm not happy when I try to fake it, no.

Chorus 2 As Chorus 1

Bridge

(A♭) G♭maj7 D♭/F E♭m7 A♭11
I wanna be high, so high,

D♭/F G♭maj7 D♭/F E♭m7 A♭11
I wan - na be free to know the things I do are right.

D♭/F G♭maj7
I wan - na be free,

D♭/F E♭m7 A♭11
Just me, whoa, baby.

Link

| E♭m7 | G♭/D♭ | E♭m7 | D♭ | D♭ ||

Guitar solo

| A♭ | Cm7 | B♭m7 | E♭11 |

| A♭ | Cm7 | B♭m7 | E♭11 |

| A♭ | Cm7 | B♭m7 | E♭11 |

| A♭ | Cm7 | B♭m7 | B♭m7 ||

Chorus 3

(B♭m7) A♭ Cm7 B♭m7
That's why I'm easy,

E♭11 A♭ Cm7 B♭m7
I'm easy like Sunday morn - ing, yeah.

E♭11 A♭ Cm7 B♭m7
That's why I'm ea - sy,__________

E♭11 A♭ Cm7 B♭m7 Bm7
I'm easy like Sunday morning,_____ whoa._____

Chorus 4

(Bm7) A C♯m7 Bm7
'Cause I'm ea - sy,

E11 A C♯m7 Bm7
Easy like Sunday morning, yeah._____

E11 A C♯m7 Bm7
'Cause I'm easy,

E11 A C♯m7 Bm7
Easy like Sunday morning, whoa._____ *To fade*

Enjoy The Silence

Words & Music by Martin Gore

Cm fr3 | E♭ fr3 | E♭m fr6 | A♭ fr4 | Fm | E♭/B♭ fr3 | B

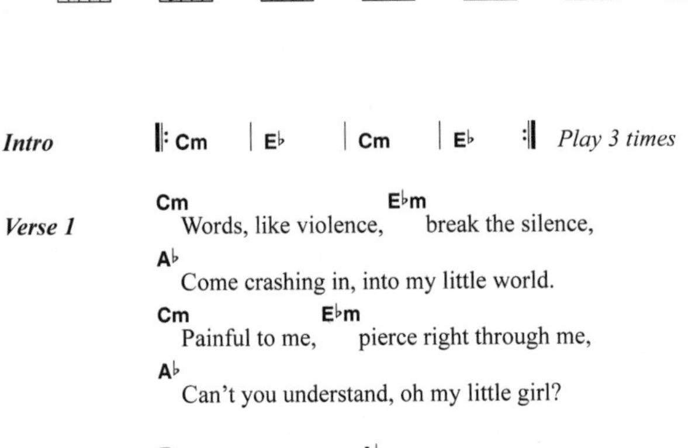

Intro ‖: Cm | E♭ | Cm | E♭ :‖ *Play 3 times*

Verse 1

```
Cm                     E♭m
   Words, like violence,    break the silence,
A♭
   Come crashing in, into my little world.
Cm              E♭m
   Painful to me,     pierce right through me,
A♭
   Can't you understand, oh my little girl?
```

Chorus 1

```
Fm                    A♭
   All I ever wanted,    all I ever needed
   Cm          E♭/B♭
Is here in my      arms.
Fm                 A♭
   Words are very unnecessary,
Cm               B
They can only do harm.
```

Link 1 | N.C. | N.C. ‖

‖: Cm | E♭ | Cm | E♭ :‖

Verse 2

```
Cm                  E♭
   Vows are spoken     to be broken,
A♭
   Feelings are intense, words are trivial.
Cm                  E♭
   Pleasures remain,    so does their pain,
A♭
   Words are meaningless and forgettable.
```

Chorus 2 As Chorus 1

Instrumental 1

```
‖: Fm     | A♭     | Cm     | E♭/B♭  :‖
‖: Cm     | E♭     | Cm     | E♭     :‖
```

Chorus 3 As Chorus 1

Chorus 4 As Chorus 1

Instrumental 2

```
‖: Fm     | A♭     | Cm     | E♭/B♭  :‖
```

Play 8 times to fade

Outro

```
N.C.
Enjoy the silence.
```

Everlasting Love

Words & Music by Buzz Cason & Mac Gayden

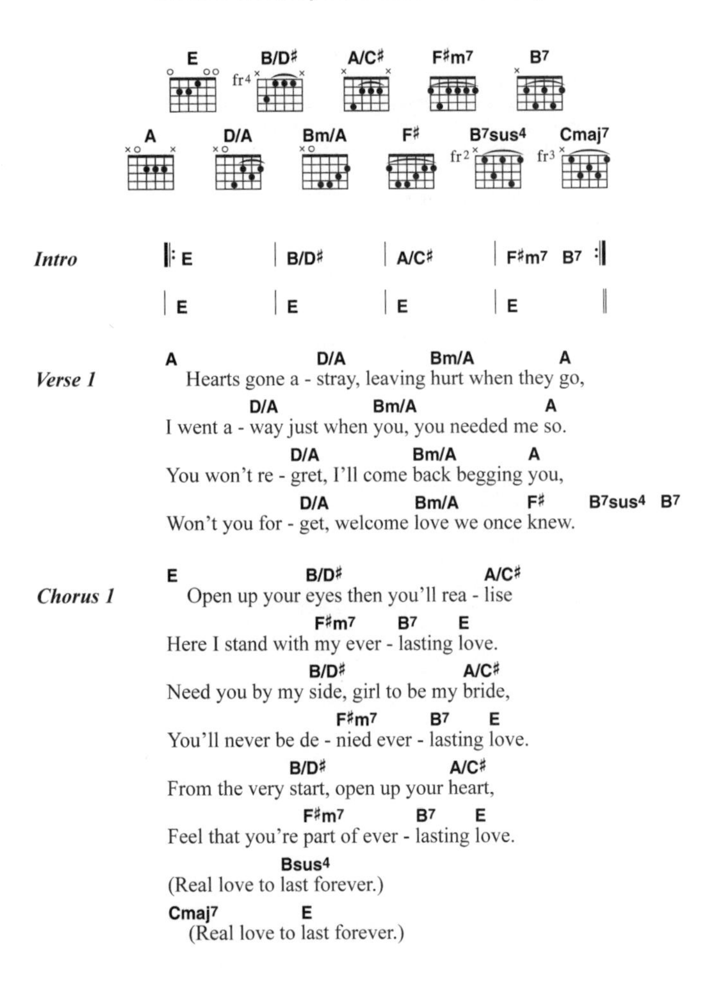

```
Instrumental  | A          | D/A        | Bm/A       | A          |
              | A          | D/A        | Bm/A       | F♯         | B7sus4  B7 ||

              E                  B/D♯                  A/C♯
Chorus 2        Where life really flows, no one really knows,
                                       F♯m7              B7     E
              Till someone's there to show the way to lasting love.
                             B/D♯                 A/C♯
              Like the sun it shines, endlessly it shines
                                  F♯m7         B7    E
              You always will be mine, it's e - ternal love.
                                   B/D♯                          A/C♯
              Whenever love went wrong, ours would still be strong,
                             F♯m7      B7     E
              We'd have our own ever - lasting love.
                          Bsus4
              (Real love to last forever.)
              Cmaj7           E
                (Real love to last forever.)

Link          | N.C.(E)    | N.C.(E)    | N.C.(E)    | N.C.(E)    ||

              E                B/D♯                    A/C♯
Chorus 3        Open up your eyes then you'll rea - lise
                                F♯m7     B7     E
              Here I stand with my ever - lasting love.
                                B/D♯                A/C♯
              Need you by my side, girl to be my bride,
                                  F♯m7        B7      E
              You'll never be de - nied ever - lasting love.
                             B/D♯               A/C♯
              From the very start, open up your heart,
                               F♯m7         B7     E
              Feel that you're part of ever - lasting love.
                                  B/D♯                           A/C♯
              Whenever love went wrong, ours would still be strong,
                             F♯m7      B7     E
              We'd have our own ever - lasting love.     To fade
```

Galveston

Words & Music by Jimmy Webb

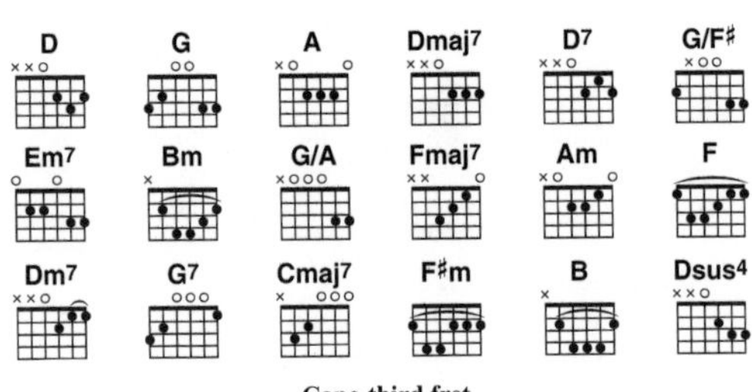

Capo third fret

Intro | D | D | D | D G A ||

Verse 1

```
D                  G     A    D
Galveston, oh Gal - ves - ton,
Dmaj7            D7          G            G/F♯   Em7
I still hear your sea winds blowin'
A       Dmaj7  D7           G           G/F♯   Em7
I still see her dark eyes glowin',
              A          Bm
She was twenty one
       G                    | G/A | D G A |
When I left Galveston.
```

Verse 2

```
D                  G     A    D
Galveston, oh Gal - ves - ton,
Dmaj7            D7          G            G/F♯   Em7
I still hear your sea waves crashing
A         Dmaj7          D7          G          G/F♯   Em7
While I watched the cannons flashing
  A         Bm
I clean my gun
       G                    | G/A | D G A |
And dream of Galveston.
```

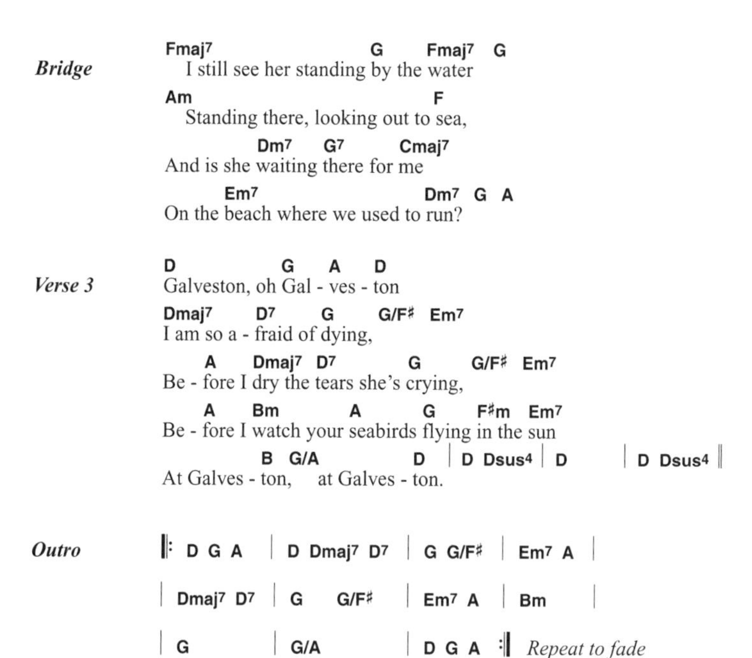
Bridge
Fmaj7 G Fmaj7 G
I still see her standing by the water
Am F
Standing there, looking out to sea,
Dm7 G7 Cmaj7
And is she waiting there for me
Em7 Dm7 G A
On the beach where we used to run?
Verse 3
D G A D
Galveston, oh Gal - ves - ton
Dmaj7 D7 G G/F♯ Em7
I am so a - fraid of dying,
A Dmaj7 D7 G G/F♯ Em7
Be - fore I dry the tears she's crying,
A Bm A G F♯m Em7
Be - fore I watch your seabirds flying in the sun
B G/A D | D Dsus4 | D | D Dsus4 ||
At Galves - ton, at Galves - ton.
Outro
: D G A	D Dmaj7 D7	G G/F♯	Em7 A
Dmaj7 D7	G G/F♯	Em7 A	Bm
G	G/A	D G A :
Repeat to fade

Geno

Words & Music by Kevin Rowland & Kevin Archer

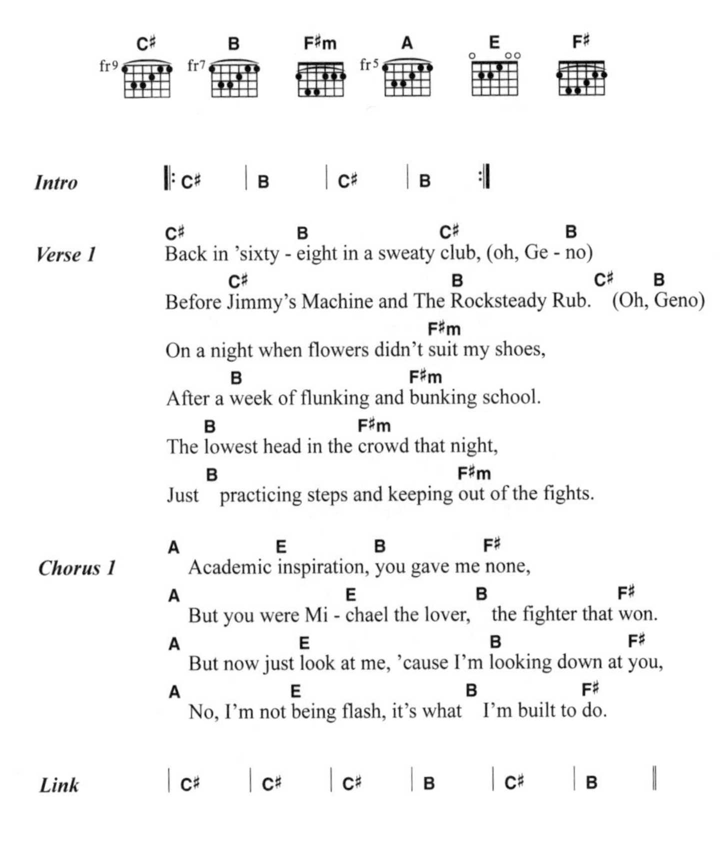

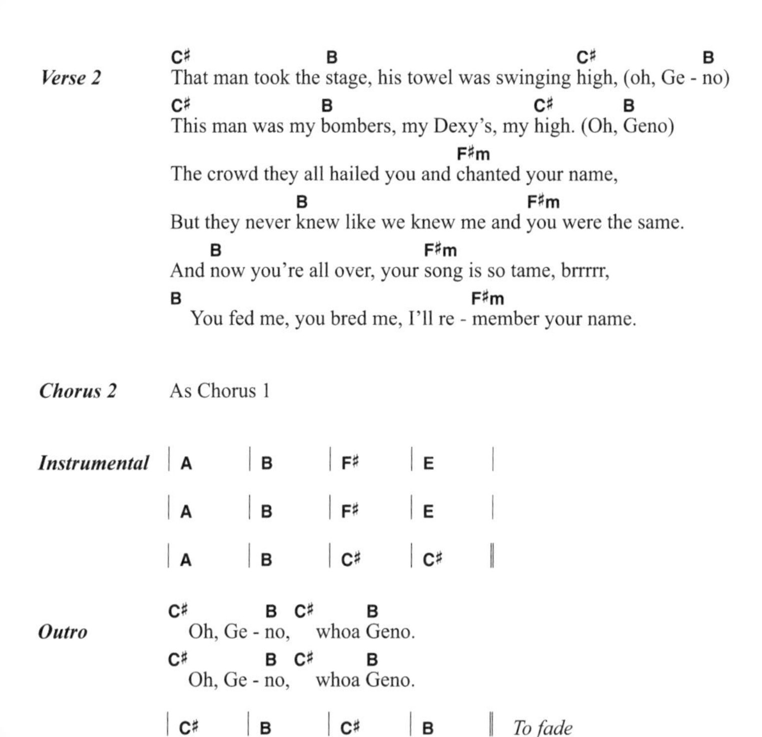
Verse 2
C♯ B C♯ B
That man took the stage, his towel was swinging high, (oh, Ge - no)
C♯ B C♯ B
This man was my bombers, my Dexy's, my high. (Oh, Geno)
F♯m
The crowd they all hailed you and chanted your name,
B F♯m
But they never knew like we knew me and you were the same.
B F♯m
And now you're all over, your song is so tame, brrrrr,
B F♯m
You fed me, you bred me, I'll re - member your name.
Chorus 2
As Chorus 1
Instrumental
A	B	F♯	E
A	B	F♯	E
A	B	C♯	C♯	
Outro
C♯ B C♯ B
Oh, Ge - no, whoa Geno.
C♯ B C♯ B
Oh, Ge - no, whoa Geno.
C♯	B	C♯	B || To fade

Groovin'

Words & Music by Felix Cavaliere & Edward Brigati Jnr.

E♭ Fm B♭7sus2 Gm7 Fm7 A♭ B♭

Intro | E♭ | Fm B♭7sus2 | E♭ | Fm B♭7sus2 ||

Verse 1

E♭ Fm B♭7sus2 E♭ Fm B♭7sus2
Groovin' on a Sunday afternoon,

E♭ Fm B♭7sus2 E♭ Fm B♭7sus2
Really couldn't get away too soon.

Gm7 Fm7
I can't imagine any - thing that's better,

Gm7 Fm7
The world is ours whenever we're together.

Gm7 Fm7 A♭ B♭
There ain't a place I'd like to be in - stead of...

Verse 2

E♭ Fm B♭7sus2 E♭ Fm B♭7sus2
Movin' down a crowded ave - nue,

E♭ Fm B♭7sus2 E♭ Fm B♭7sus2
Doing any - thing we like to do.

Gm7 Fm7
There's always lots of things that we can see,

Gm7 Fm7
We can be anyone we like to be.

Gm7 Fm7 A♭ B♭
All those happy people we could meet just...

Verse 3

E♭ Fm B♭7sus2 E♭ Fm B♭7sus2
Groovin' on a Sunday after - noon,

E♭ Fm B♭7sus2 E♭ Fm B♭7sus2
Really, couldn't get away too soon. No, no, no, no.

Interlude

E♭ Fm B♭7sus2
Ah, ha, ha.________

E♭ Fm B♭7sus2
Ah, ha, ha.________

E♭ Fm B♭7sus2
Ah, ha, ha.________

Bridge

Gm7 Fm7
We'll keep on spending sunny days this way,

Gm7 Fm7
We're gonna talk and laugh our time away.

Gm7 Fm7
I feel it coming closer day by day,

A♭ Gm7 Fm7 B♭
Life would be ec - stasy, you and me end - lessly

Verse 4

E♭ Fm B♭7sus2 E♭ Fm B♭7sus2
Groovin' on a Sunday after - noon,

E♭ Fm B♭7sus2 E♭ Fm B♭7sus2
Really couldn't get away too soon. No, no, no, no.

E♭ Fm B♭7sus2
Groovin', ah, ha, ah, ha,

E♭ Fm B♭7sus2
Groovin'. *To fade*

Halfway To Paradise

Words & Music by Carole King & Gerry Goffin

D A/D A G D/A Bm E Em

Intro | D | D | D A/D D A/D | D ||

Verse 1
```
D
I want to be your lover,
                        A
But your friend is all I've stayed.
          D          G
I'm only halfway to paradise,
   D        A        D
So near, yet so far a - way.
```

Verse 2
```
 G    A D
I long for your lips to kiss my lips,
                         A
But just when I think they may,
               D          G
You lead me halfway to paradise,
   D/A      A        D
So near, yet so far a - way.
```

Bridge
```
N.C.  A                               D
Mmm, being close to you is almost heaven,
   A                         D
But seeing you can do just so much.
  A                                 D
It hurts me so to know your heart's a treasure,
            Bm      E               Em    A
And that my heart   is forbidden to touch.
```

```
            N.C.          D
*Verse 3*   So, put your sweet lips close to my lips
                                                           A
            And tell me that's where they're gonna stay.
                           D           G
            Don't leave me halfway to paradise,
               D/A      A        D
            So near, yet so far a - way.
                         G       D/A       A        D
            Whoa, whoa, oh, so near, yet so far a - way.
                          G           D/A       A        D
            Mmm, mmm, mmm, so near, yet so far a - way.    To fade
```

Heartbreak Hotel

Words & Music by Elvis Presley, Mae Boren Axton & Tommy Durden

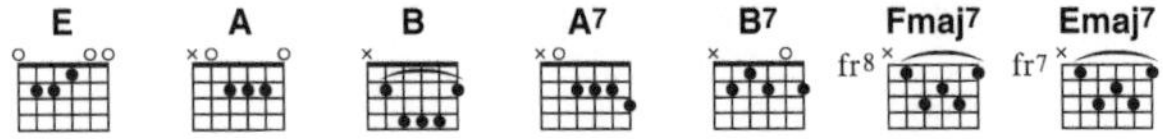

E A B A7 B7 Fmaj7 (fr8) Emaj7 (fr7)

Verse 1

N.C. **(E)**
Well since my baby left me,
N.C. **(E)**
Well I've found a new place to dwell,
N.C.
But it's down at the end of Lonely Street,

At Heartbreak Hotel, where I'll be,

Chorus 1

(A)
I'll be so lonely, baby,

I may get so lonely,
(B) **(E)**
I may get so lonely I could die.

Verse 2

N.C. **(E)**
Although it's always crowded
N.C. **(E)**
You still can find some room
N.C.
For broken-hearted lovers

To cry there in the gloom.

Chorus 2

A7
Well they get so lonely, baby,

Well they get so lonely,
B7 **E**
They'll get so lonely they could die.

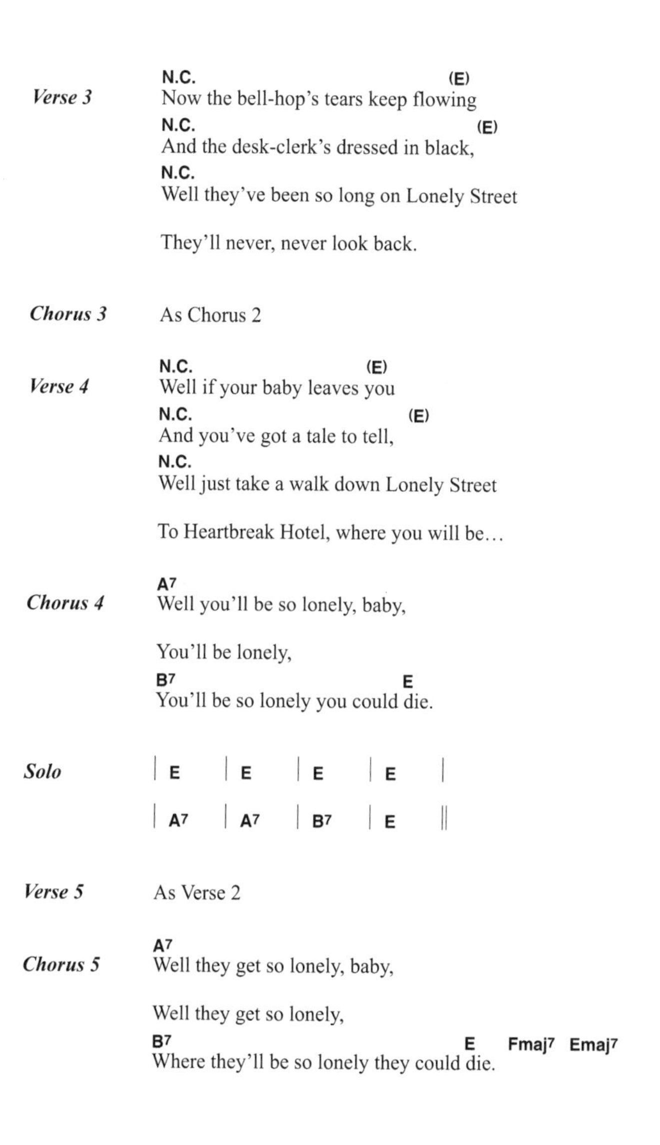

Verse 3

N.C. (E)
Now the bell-hop's tears keep flowing
N.C. (E)
And the desk-clerk's dressed in black,
N.C.
Well they've been so long on Lonely Street

They'll never, never look back.

Chorus 3

As Chorus 2

Verse 4

N.C. (E)
Well if your baby leaves you
N.C. (E)
And you've got a tale to tell,
N.C.
Well just take a walk down Lonely Street

To Heartbreak Hotel, where you will be…

Chorus 4

A7
Well you'll be so lonely, baby,

You'll be lonely,
B7 E
You'll be so lonely you could die.

Solo

| E | E | E | E |
| A7 | A7 | B7 | E ||

Verse 5

As Verse 2

Chorus 5

A7
Well they get so lonely, baby,

Well they get so lonely,
B7 E Fmaj7 Emaj7
Where they'll be so lonely they could die.

Hounds Of Love

Words & Music by Kate Bush

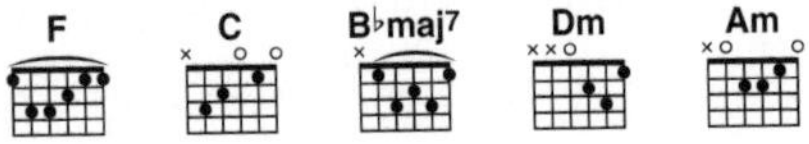

F   C   B♭maj7   Dm   Am

Intro *It's in the trees, it's coming!*

Verse 1

F C B♭maj7
When I was a child, running in the night,
F
Afraid of what might be.
C B♭maj7
Hiding in the dark, hiding in the street
Dm C
And of what was following me.

Pre-chorus 1

B♭maj7 Am Dm B♭maj7
Now hounds of love are hunting,
Am C Dm B♭maj7
I've always been a coward.
Am C Dm
And I don't know what's good for me.

Chorus 1

(Dm) F
Oh, here I go,
B♭maj7
It's coming for me through the trees,
F B♭maj7
Oh, help me someone, help me please.
F B♭maj7
And take my shoes off and throw them in the lake,
F B♭maj7
And I'll be___ two steps on the water.

Verse 2

F C B♭maj7
I found a fox caught by dogs,
F
He let me take him in my hands,
C B♭maj7
His little heart, it beats so fast.

cont.

F
And I'm ashamed of running a - way,
C B♭maj7
From nothing real, I just can't deal with this,
Dm C
I'm still afraid to be there.

Pre-chorus 2

B♭maj7 Am Dm B♭maj7
Among your hounds of love.
Am C Dm B♭maj7
And feel yours arms surround me.
Am C Dm B♭maj7
I've always been a coward,
Am C Dm
And never know what's good for me.

Chorus 2

(Dm) F
Oh, here I go,
B♭maj7 F
Don't let me go, hold me down,
B♭maj7
It's coming for me through the trees,
F B♭maj7
Oh, help me darling, help me please.
F B♭maj7
Take my shoes off and throw them in the lake,
F B♭maj7
And I'll be___ two steps on the water.
F
I don't know what's good for me,
B♭maj7
I don't know what's good for me,

I need la, la, la, love, love,
F B♭maj7
Yeah, your, yeah, your, your love.
F B♭maj7
And take your shoes off and throw them in the lake.
F
Do you know what I really need,
B♭maj7
Do you know what I really need?
F
La, la, la love, love, yeah.

I Can Help

Words & Music by Billy Swan

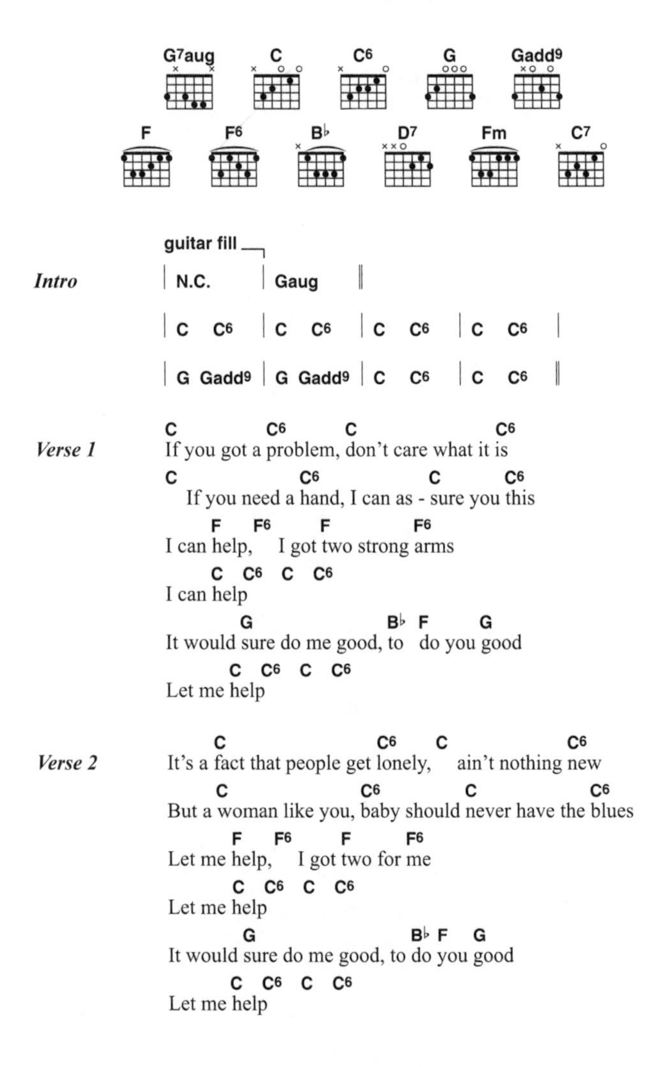

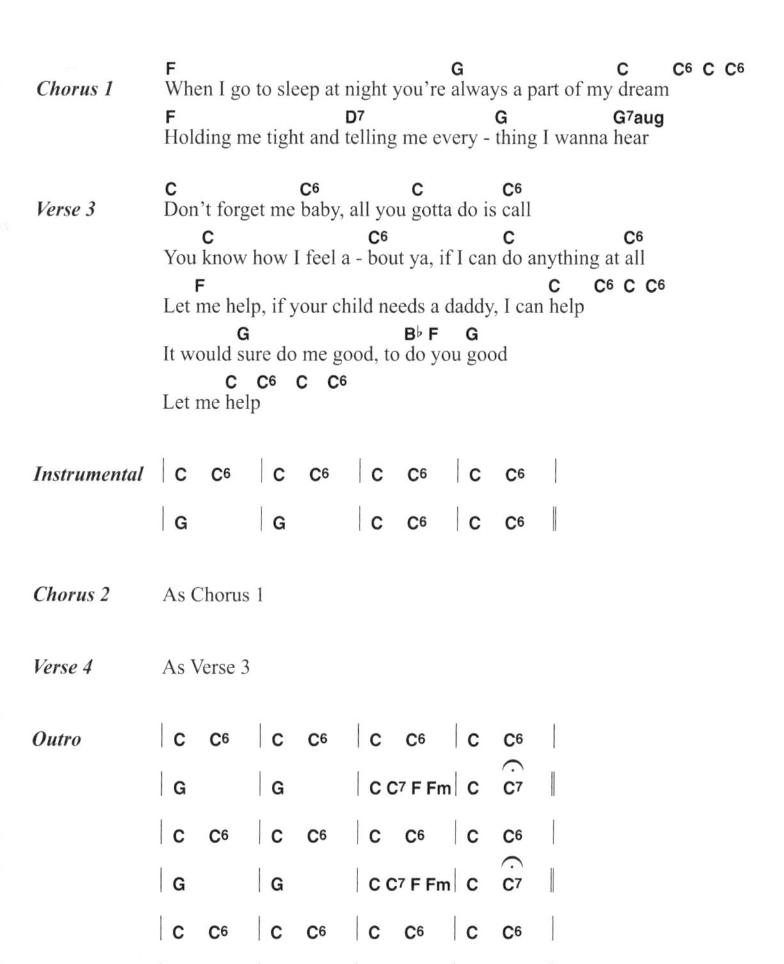

Chorus 1

F G C C6 C C6
When I go to sleep at night you're always a part of my dream
F D7 G G7aug
Holding me tight and telling me every - thing I wanna hear

Verse 3

C C6 C C6
Don't forget me baby, all you gotta do is call
C C6 C C6
You know how I feel a - bout ya, if I can do anything at all
F C C6 C C6
Let me help, if your child needs a daddy, I can help
G B♭ F G
It would sure do me good, to do you good
C C6 C C6
Let me help

Instrumental

| C C6 | C C6 | C C6 | C C6 |
| G | G | C C6 | C C6 ||

Chorus 2

As Chorus 1

Verse 4

As Verse 3

Outro

C C6	C C6	C C6	C C6
G	G	C C7 F Fm	C C7 (fermata)	
C C6	C C6	C C6	C C6
G	G	C C7 F Fm	C C7 (fermata)	
C C6	C C6	C C6	C C6
G	G	C C7 F Fm	C C7 || *Fade*

I Don't Feel Like Dancin'

Words & Music by Elton John, Scott Hoffman & Jason Sellards

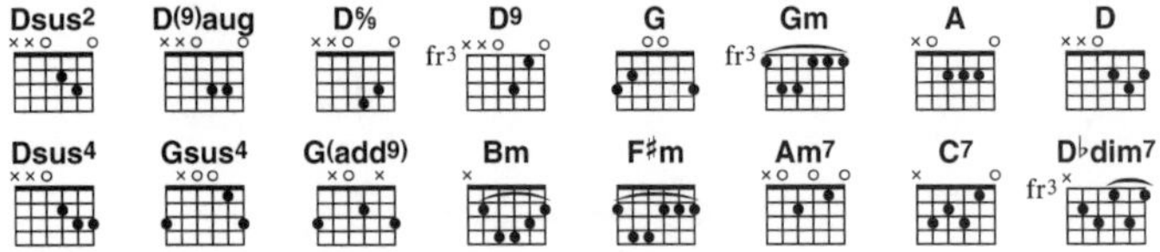

Dsus2 D(9)aug D% D9 G Gm A D

Dsus4 Gsus4 G(add9) Bm F♯m Am7 C7 D♭dim7

Intro | Dsus2 | D(9)aug | D% | D9 |
| G | Gm | A | A |
| D Dsus4 D | D Dsus4 D | D Dsus4 | D Dsus4 D ||

Verse 1
D Dsus4 D Dsus4 D
Wake up in the morn - ing with a head like 'what ya done?'
G Gsus4 G G(add9) G Gsus4 G(add9) G
This used to be the life but I don't need another one.
D Dsus4 D Dsus4 D
You like cuttin' up and carrying on, you wear them gowns.
G Gsus4 G G(add9) G Gsus4 G(add9) G
So how come I feel so lonely when you're up getting down?

Bridge 1
Bm F♯m
So I'll play along when I hear that special song,
Am7 G
I'm gonna be the one who gets it right.
Bm F♯m
You better move when you're swayin' 'round the room,
Am G
Look's like magic's only ours to - night.

Pre-chorus 1
D Dsus4 D Dsus4 D
But I don't feel like danc - in' when the old Joanna plays,
G Gsus4 G G(add9) G
My heart could take a chance, but my two feet can't find a way.
A C7 G
You'd think that I could muster up a little soft-shoe gentle sway,
D Dsus4 D
But I don't feel like danc - in', no sir, no dancin' today.

Chorus 1

D
Don't feel like dancin', dancin',

Even if I find nothin' better to do.

G
Don't feel like dancin', dancin',

Why'd you pick a tune when I'm not in the mood?

A
Don't feel like dancin', dancin',

C7 G D Dsus4 D
I'd rather be home with the one in the bed till dawn with you.

Instrumental 1

| Gm G | C7 | Gm G | C7 |

| Gm G | C7 D♭dim7 | D Dsus4 D | D Dsus4 D ||

Verse 2

D Dsus4 D Dsus4 D
Cities come and ci - ties go just like the old em - pires,

G Gsus4 G G(add9) G G(add9)
When all you do is change your clothes and call that versatile.

D Dsus4 D Dsus4 D
You got so many col - ours, make a blind man so confused,

G Gsus4 G G(add9)
Then why can't I keep up when you're the only thing I lose?

Bridge 2

Bm F♯m
So I'll just pretend that I know which way to bend,

Am7 G
And I'm gonna tell the whole world that you're mine.

Bm F♯m
Just please understand when I see you clap your hands,

Am G
If you stick around I'm sure that I'll be fine.

Pre-chorus 2 As Pre-chorus 1

Chorus 2 As Chorus 1

Instrumental 2 | **Bm** | **F♯m** | **Am7** | **G** |
| **Bm** | **F♯m** | **Am7** | **G** ‖

Middle

```
D                          D(9)aug
You can't make me dance around,
    D%                       D7
But your two-step makes my chest pound.
              G              Gm                   A
Just lay me down as you float away into the shimmer light.
```

Pre-chorus 3 As Pre-chorus 1

Chorus 3 As Chorus 1

Chorus 4 As Chorus 1

Outro | **D Dsus4 D** | **D Dsus4 D** | **D Dsus4 D** | **D Dsus4 D** ‖

I Want You Back

Words & Music by Berry Gordy, Deke Richards,
Alphonso Mizell & Freddie Perren

G C Em Bm

Am D D/F♯ G/B C/E

fr3

Capo first fret

Intro ‖: G | G | C | C |
| Em Bm | C G | Am D | G :‖

G D/F♯ Em D C G/B
Uh - huh,___ huh, huh,______

Am D Em Bm C G Am D G
Let me tell you now, huh - huh.

Verse 1

G C
When I had you to myself, I didn't want you around,

Em Bm C G Am D G
Those pretty faces always made you stand out in a crowd.

C
But someone picked you from the bunch, one glance was all it took,

Em Bm C G Am D G
Now it's much too late for me to take a second look.

Chorus 1

G D/F♯ Em D C G/B Am D
Oh baby, give me one more chance,___ (show you that I love you)

Em Bm C G Am D G
Won't you please let me___ back in your heart.

D/F♯ Em D C G/B Am D
Oh darlin', I was blind to let you go, (let you go baby)

Em Bm C G Am D G
But now since I see you in his arms.

cont.

(I want you back) Oh, I do now.

(I want you back) Ooh, ooh baby.

(I want you back) Yeah, yeah, yeah, yeah.

(I want you back) Na, na, na, na.

Verse 2

```
G                                           C
Tryin' to live without your love is one long sleepless night,
Em      Bm         C    G        Am      D          G
Let me show you girl,___ that I know wrong from right.
                                           C
Every street you walk on, I leave tear stains on the ground,
Em        Bm     C    G              Am   D        G
Follow - ing the girl___ I didn't even want a - round.

Let me tell you now.
```

Chorus 2

```
G  D/F♯  Em  D        C          G/B       Am                D
Oh baby, all I need is one more chance, (show you that I love you)
Em    Bm C       G  Am  D  G
Won't you please let me___ back in your heart.
   D/F♯    Em    D        C       G/B Am        D
Oh darlin', I was blind to let you go, (let you go baby)
     Em  Bm   C G                 D/F♯  C/E    G
But now since I   see you in his arms.     Oh.___
```

Bridge

```
| G  D/F♯ | C/E  G | G  D/F♯ | C/E  G |

G  D/F♯  C/E  G
A - buh, buh,  buh, buh.
   D/F♯  C/E  G
A - buh, buh,  buh, buh.
                D/F♯  C/E  G
All I want, (a - buh, buh,  buh, buh)
                D/F♯  C/E  G
All I need, (a - buh, buh,  buh, buh)
                D/F♯  C/E  G
All I want, (a - buh, buh,  buh, buh)

All I need.
```

Chorus 3

```
G  D/F#  Em     D          C       G/B  Am              D
    Oh,        just one more chance to    show you that I love you,
Em    Bm   C    G           Am  D     G
Baby, baby, baby, baby, ba - by,   baby.
```

(I want you back)

Forget what happened then, let me live again.

Chorus 4

```
G  D/F#  Em    D          C       G/B   Am D
Oh baby, I was blind to let you go,
    Em  Bm    C G   Am D     G
But now since I   see you in his arms.
```

(I want you back)

Spare me of this cause, give me what I lost.

Chorus 5

```
G  D/F#  Em     D           C        G/B  Am           D
Oh baby, I need one more chance, ha, I tell ya that I love you,
 Em     Bm  C       G          Am  D
(Baby,) ow, (baby,) ow, (ba - by.)  oh.
  G
I want you back, I want you back.    To fade
```

I Never Loved A Man (The Way I Love You)

Words & Music by Ronny Shannon

F B♭7 C7 C7sus4 C7♯9 A♭7
fr4

Intro | F B♭7 | F B♭7 | F B♭7 | F B♭7 ‖

Verse 1
(B♭7) F B♭7 F B♭7 F
You're a no good heartbreaker,
B♭7 F B♭7 F
You're a liar and you're a cheat.
B♭7 F B♭7
And I don't know why
C7 C7sus4 C7
I let you do these things to me.
F B♭7 F B♭7 F
My friends keep telling me
B♭7 F B♭7
That you ain't no good,
F B♭7 F B♭7
But oh, but they don't know
C7 C7sus4 C7
That I'd leave you if I could.

Chorus 1
C7 C7sus4 C7 C7sus4 C7
I guess I'm up - tight
C7sus4 C7
And I'm stuck like glue,
C7♯9 F B♭7
'Cause I ain't never,
F B♭7 F B♭7 C7
I ain't never, I ain't never, no, no,
N.C. F B♭7 F B♭7
Loved a man the way that I, I love you.

Verse 2
F B♭7 F B♭7 F
Some time a - go I thought
B♭7 F B♭7 F
You had run out of fools,

cont.

B♭7 F B♭7
But I was so wrong,
C7 C7sus4 C7
You got one that you'll never lose.
F B♭7 F B♭7 F
The way you treat me is a shame,
B♭7 F B♭7
How could you hurt me so bad?
F B♭7 F B♭7
Baby, you know that I'm the best thing
C7 C7sus4 C7
That you ever had.

Chorus 2

C7 C7sus4 C7 C7sus4 C7
Kiss me once a - gain,
C7sus4 C7
Don't you never, never say that we're through,
C7♯9 F B♭7
'Cause I ain't never,
F B♭7 F B♭7 C7
Never, never, no, no,
N.C. F B♭7 F
Loved a man the way that I, I love you.

Bridge

B♭7
I can't sleep at night

And I can't eat a bite.
F
I guess I'll never be free,
C7
Since you got your hooks in me.

Whoa, oh, oh.
B♭7 A♭7
Yeah, yeah.

Outro

F B♭7 F
I ain't never loved a man,
B♭7 F B♭7 F
I ain't never loved a man, baby,
B♭7 F B♭7 F
Ain't never had a man that hurt me so bad.
B♭7
No.
F B♭7 F
Well this is what I'm gonna do about it. *To fade*

I Only Have Eyes For You

Words by Al Dubin
Music by Harry Warren

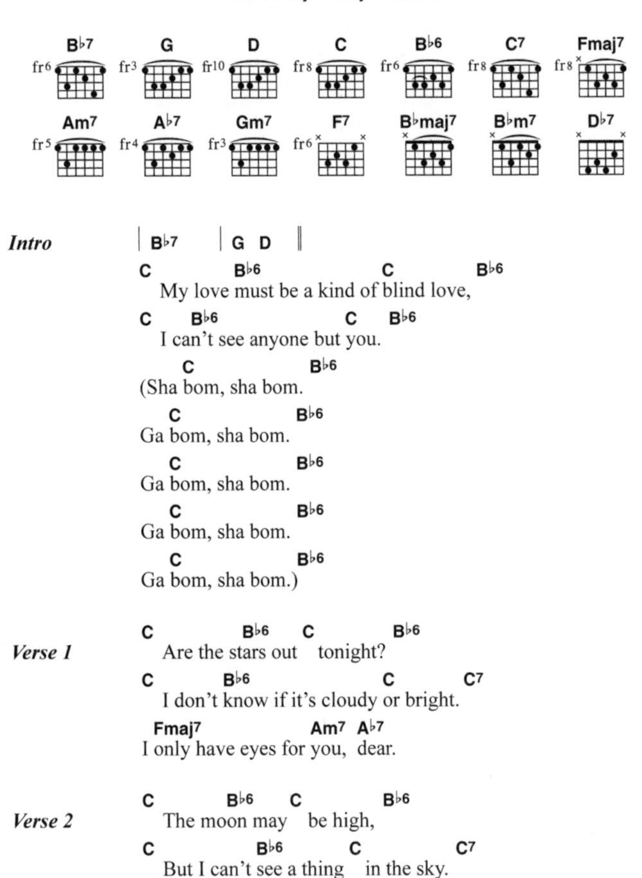

Intro | B♭7 | G D ||

```
C              B♭6                C                B♭6
  My love must be a kind of blind love,
C      B♭6                C     B♭6
  I can't see anyone but you.
    C              B♭6
(Sha bom, sha bom.
   C              B♭6
Ga bom, sha bom.
   C              B♭6
Ga bom, sha bom.
   C              B♭6
Ga bom, sha bom.
   C              B♭6
Ga bom, sha bom.)
```

Verse 1

```
C              B♭6    C           B♭6
  Are the stars out   tonight?
C            B♭6                  C          C7
  I don't know if it's cloudy or bright.
 Fmaj7                   Am7  A♭7
I only have eyes for you, dear.
```

Verse 2

```
C            B♭6     C          B♭6
  The moon may   be high,
C               B♭6        C            C7
  But I can't see a thing   in the sky.
 Fmaj7                  D7
I only have eyes for you.
```

Bridge

```
Gm7               C7               Fmaj7    F7
   I don't know if we're in a garden
B♭maj7     B♭m7           Fmaj7     D♭7
   Or on a crowded ave - nue.
```

Verse 3

```
C             B♭6  C              B♭6
   You are here    and so am I,
C                B♭6                C         C7
   Maybe mil - lions of people    go by.
            Fmaj7               D7
But they all disappear from view
        Gm7              C7  N.C.
And I only have eyes___  for you.
```

Outro

```
       C                B♭6
𝄆 (Ga bom, sha bom.)        𝄇   Repeat to fade
```

I'm Waiting For The Man

Words & Music by Lou Reed

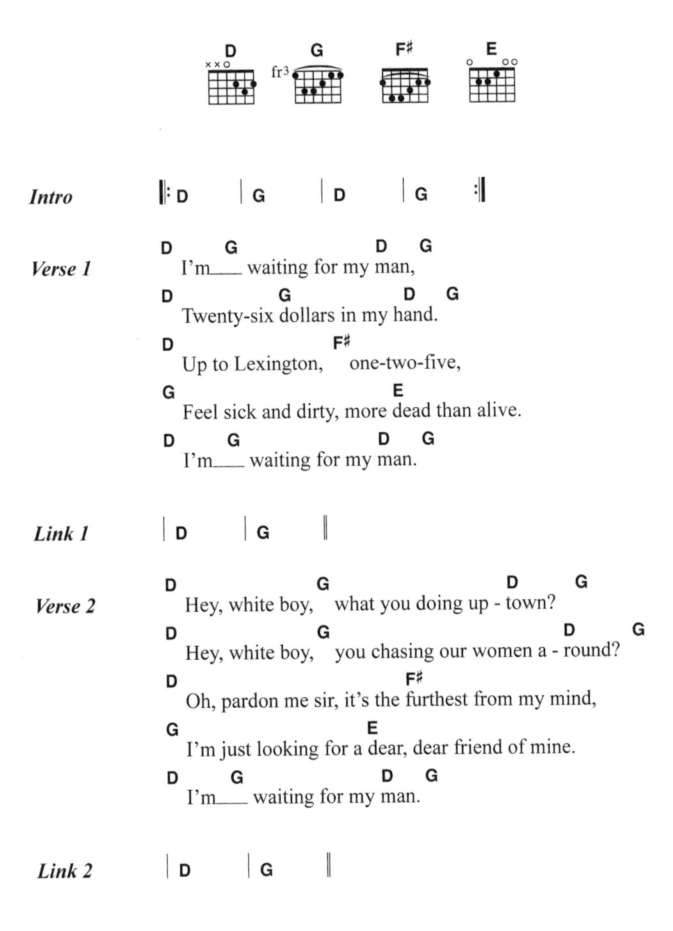

Intro

|: D | G | D | G :|

Verse 1

D G D G
I'm___ waiting for my man,
D G D G
Twenty-six dollars in my hand.
D F♯
Up to Lexington, one-two-five,
G E
Feel sick and dirty, more dead than alive.
D G D G
I'm___ waiting for my man.

Link 1

| D | G ||

Verse 2

D G D G
Hey, white boy, what you doing up - town?
D G D G
Hey, white boy, you chasing our women a - round?
D F♯
Oh, pardon me sir, it's the furthest from my mind,
G E
I'm just looking for a dear, dear friend of mine.
D G D G
I'm___ waiting for my man.

Link 2

| D | G ||

Verse 3

```
D                   G                   D      G
   Here he comes,    he's all dressed in black,
D              G                D    G
   P.R. shoes    and a big straw hat.
D                    F♯
   He's never early, he's always late,
G                                 E
First thing you learn is that you always gotta wait.
D       G               D    G
   I'm___ waiting for my man.    Oh, work it now.
```

Instrumental ‖: D | G | D | G :‖ *Play 5 times*

Verse 4

```
D                        G                      D      G
   Up to a Brownstone,    up three flights of stairs,
D                              G               D     G
   Everybody's pinned you,    but nobody cares.
D                          F♯
   He's got the works, gives you sweet taste,
   G                                             E
Ah, then you gotta split because you got no time to waste.
D       G               D    G
   I'm___ waiting for my man.
```

Link 3 | D | G | D | G ‖

Verse 5

```
D                              G                             D      G
   Baby, don't you holler, darling, don't you bawl and shout,
D                        G                                  D    G
   I'm feeling good,    you know I'm gonna work it on out.
D                         F♯
   I'm feeling good, I feel oh, so fine,
   G                           E
Until tomorrow, but that's just some other time.
D       G               D    G
I'm___ waiting for my man.    Walk it home.
```

Outro ‖: D | G | D | G :‖ *Play 8 times to fade*

Just My Imagination (Running Away With Me)

Words & Music by Norman J. Whitfield & Barrett Strong

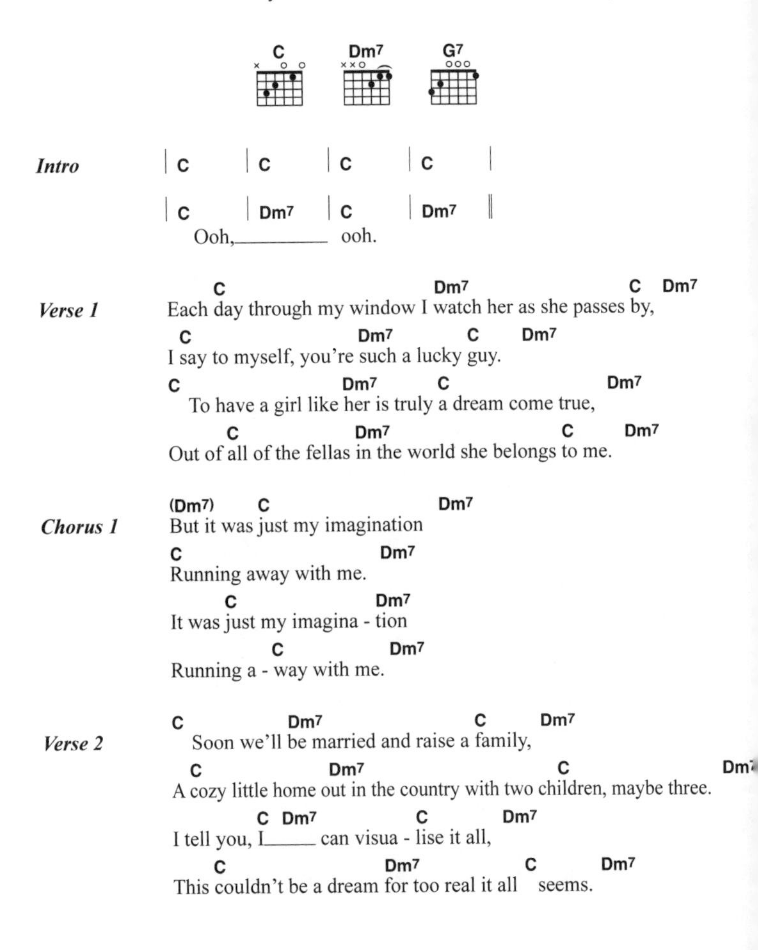

Intro

| C | C | C | C |

| C | Dm7 | C | Dm7 ||
Ooh,_________ ooh.

Verse 1

C Dm7 C Dm7
Each day through my window I watch her as she passes by,
C Dm7 C Dm7
I say to myself, you're such a lucky guy.
C Dm7 C Dm7
To have a girl like her is truly a dream come true,
C Dm7 C Dm7
Out of all of the fellas in the world she belongs to me.

Chorus 1

(Dm7) C Dm7
But it was just my imagination
C Dm7
Running away with me.
C Dm7
It was just my imagina - tion
C Dm7
Running a - way with me.

Verse 2

C Dm7 C Dm7
Soon we'll be married and raise a family,
C Dm7 C Dm7
A cozy little home out in the country with two children, maybe three.
C Dm7 C Dm7
I tell you, I_____ can visua - lise it all,
C Dm7 C Dm7
This couldn't be a dream for too real it all seems.

Chorus 2

(Dm7) C Dm7
But it was just my imagination, once again
C Dm7
Running away with me.
C Dm7
I tell you it was just my imagina - tion
C Dm7
Running a - way with me.

Bridge

C
Every night, on my knees I pray,

Dear Lord, hear my plea,

Don't ever let another take her love from me
G7
Or I will surely die.
C
Ooh, her love is heavenly,

When her arms enfold me

I hear a tender rhapsody.

But in reality, she doesn't even know me.

Chorus 3

C Dm7
Just my imagination, once again
C Dm7
Running away with me.
C Dm7
Oh, I tell you it was just my imagina - tion
C
Running a - way with me.
Dm7
I never met her but I can't forget her.
C Dm7
Just my imagination, ooh, yeah, yeah, yeah, yeah,
C
Running away with me
Dm7 C Dm7
Ooh, just my imagina - tion
C
Running a - way with me. *To fade*

Karma Chameleon

Words & Music by George O'Dowd, Roy Hay,
Michael Craig, Jon Moss & Phil Pickett

Verse 2
B♭ F B♭
Didn't hear your wicked words every day,
F B♭ B♭
And you used to be so sweet, I heard you say
E♭ F
That my love was an ad - diction,
E♭ F
When we cling our love is strong,
E♭ F
When you go you're gone for - ever.
Cm7
You string a - long,
Gm F
You string a - long.
Chorus 2
As Chorus 1
Bridge 2
E♭ Dm7
Every day is like sur - vival,
Cm7 Gm7
You're my lover not my rival.
E♭ Dm7
Every day is like sur - vival,
Cm7 Gm F
You're my lover not my ri - val.
Harmonica solo
| B♭ | F | B♭ | B♭ |
| B♭ | F | B♭ | B♭ ||
(I'm a)

```
              E♭                 F
*Verse 3*     I'm a man without con - viction,
              E♭                 F
              I'm a man who doesn't know,
                E♭              F
              How to sell a contra - dication.
                           Cm7
              You come and go,
                           Gm   F
              You come and go.

                B♭                                   F/A          Gm
*Chorus 3*    ‖: Karma, karma, karma, karma, karma chamel - eon,
                           Cm7
              You come and go,
                           B♭/F  F
              You come and go.
              B♭                              Dm7              Gm
              Loving would be easy if your colours were like my dream
                           Cm7
              Red, gold and green,
                           B♭/F  F
              Red, gold and green.      :‖ Repeat 4 times and fade
```

Last Train To Clarksville

Words & Music by Tommy Boyce & Bobby Hart

G G7 G6 C7 D7 G9sus4 G5

Intro ‖: G | G7 G6 | G | G7 G6 :‖

Verse 1

(G6) G G7
Take the last train to Clarksville

G6 G G7
And I'll meet you at the station,

G6 G G7
You can be here by four thirty,

G6 G G7 G6 C7
'Cause I've made your reser - vation, don't be slow.

N.C.
Oh, no, no, no, oh, no, no, no.

Verse 2

N.C. G G7
'Cause I'm leaving in the morning

G6 G G7
And I must see you a - gain,

G6 G G7
We'll have one more night to - gether,

G6 G G7 G6 C7
Till the morning brings my train and I must go.

N.C.
Oh, no, no, no, oh, no, no, no,

D7 (G)
And I don't know if I'm ever coming home.

Link 1 | G | G7 G6 | G | G7 G6 ‖

Verse 3

(G6) G G7
Take the last train to Clarksville,

G6 G G7
I'll be waiting at the station,

G6 G G7 G6
We'll have time for coffee - flavored kisses,

G G7 C7 C7
And a bit of conver - sation, oh.

N.C.
Oh, no, no, no, oh, no, no, no.

Bridge 1

G G9sus4
Du du du du du du du du, du du du du du du du du,

G5 G9sus4
Du du du du du du du du.

G G9sus4
Du du du du du du du du, du du du du du du du du,

G5 G9sus4
Du du du du du du du du.

Verse 4

N.C. G G7
Take the last train to Clarksville,

G6 G G7
Now I must hang up the phone,

G6 G G7 G6 G
I can't hear you in this noisy railroad station,

G7 G6 C7
All a - lone, I'm feeling low.

N.C.
Oh, no, no, no, oh, no, no, no,

D7 (G)
And I don't know if I'm ever coming home.

Bridge 2

|: G | G9sus4 | G | G9sus4 :|

| G | G9sus4 | G | G9sus4 |
Ah.________________________________

| G | G9sus4 | G | G9sus4 N.C. ||
(ah)________________________________

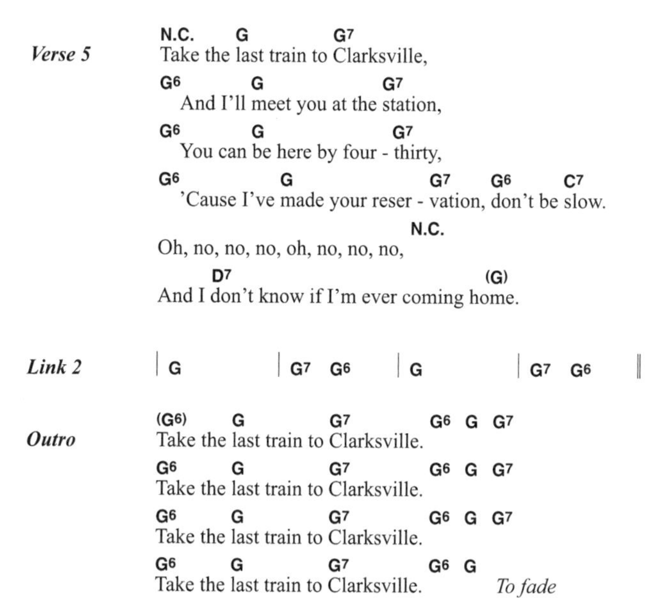

Verse 5

N.C. G G7
Take the last train to Clarksville,
G6 G G7
And I'll meet you at the station,
G6 G G7
You can be here by four - thirty,
G6 G G7 G6 C7
'Cause I've made your reser - vation, don't be slow.
N.C.
Oh, no, no, no, oh, no, no, no,
D7 (G)
And I don't know if I'm ever coming home.

Link 2

| G | G7 G6 | G | G7 G6 ‖

Outro

(G6) G G7 G6 G G7
Take the last train to Clarksville.
G6 G G7 G6 G G7
Take the last train to Clarksville.
G6 G G7 G6 G G7
Take the last train to Clarksville.
G6 G G7 G6 G
Take the last train to Clarksville. *To fade*

Life On Mars?

Words & Music by David Bowie

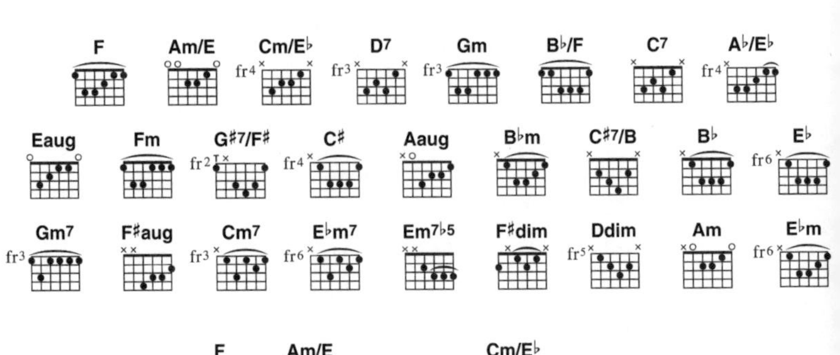

Verse 1

```
   F        Am/E                    Cm/E♭
   It's a god-awful small affair
           D7
To the girl with the mousey hair
Gm          B♭/F                      C7
   But her mummy is yelling "No,"
                                F
And her daddy has told her to go.
          Am/E                      Cm/E♭
But her friend is nowhere to be seen
            D7
Now she walks through her sunken dream
Gm         B♭/F                        C7
   To the seat with the clearest view

And she's hooked to the silver screen.
```

Pre-chorus 1

```
A♭/E♭       Eaug                  Fm
   But the film is a saddening bore
              G♯7/F♯
For she's lived it ten times or more.
C♯                Aaug                   B♭m
   She could spit in the eyes of fools
            C♯7/B
As they ask her to focus on:
```

Chorus 1

B♭ E♭
Sailors fighting in the dance hall,
Gm7 F♯aug F
Oh man! Look at those cavemen go.
Fm Cm7
It's the freakiest show.
E♭m7 B♭
Take a look at the Lawman
E♭
Beating up the wrong guy.
Gm F♯aug
Oh man! Wonder if he'll ever know
F Fm Cm7
He's in the best-selling show?
E♭m7 Gm7 F♯aug B♭/F Em7♭5
Is there life on Mars?________________

Link

| F F♯dim | Gm Ddim | Am B♭ | B♭m ||

Verse 2

F Am/E Cm/E♭
It's on Amerika's tortured brow
D7
That Mickey Mouse has grown up a cow.
Gm B♭/F C7
Now the workers have struck for fame

'Cause Lennon's on sale again.
F Am/E Cm/E♭
See the mice in their million hordes
D7 Gm
From Ibiza to the Norfolk Broads.
B♭/F C7
'Rule Britannia' is out of bounds

To my mother, my dog, and clowns.

Pre-chorus 2

A♭/E♭ Eaug Fm
But the film is a saddening bore
G♯7/F♯
'Cause I wrote it ten times or more.
C♯ Aaug B♭m
It's about to be writ again
C♯7/B
As I ask you to focus on:

Chorus 2

As Chorus 1

Coda

| F F♯dim | Gm B♭/F | B♭/F | E♭ E♭m | B♭ ||

The Look Of Love

Words & Music by Mark White, Martin Fry & Stephen Singleton

F G Am F/A G/A Em/A Em

Intro | F G | Am G | F G | Am G |

F G Am G
Ah,___ ah,

F G Am G Am
Mmm, mmm, whoa, whoa, whoa.

Verse 1

(Am) F/A G/A Em/A F/A
When your world is full of strange ar - rangements

G/A Em/A F/A
And gravity won't pull you through.

G/A Em/A F/A
You know you're miss - ing out on something,

G/A Em/A F/A
Well, that something de - pends on you.

Pre-chorus 1

F G
(All I'm saying,)

Em F
It takes a lot to love you.

G
(All I'm doing,)

Em F
You know it's true.

G
(All I need now),

Em F
There's one thing, yes, one thing

G Em F
That turns this grey sky to blue.

Chorus 1

F G Am
(That's the look, that's the look,)
G F
The look of love.
G Am
(That's the look, that's the look,)
G F
The look of love.
G Am
(That's the look, that's the look,)
G F G Am G Am
The look of love.____________

Verse 2

(Am) F/A G/A Em/A F/A
When your girl has left you out on the pavement,
G/A Em/A F/A
When your dreams fall apart at the seams.
G/A Em/A F/A
Your reason for living, your reason for leaving,
G/A Em/A F/A
Don't ask me what it means.

Pre-chorus 2

(F/A) F
(Who got the look?)
G Em F
I don't know the answer to that question.

(Where's the look?)
G Em F
If I knew I would tell you.

(What's the look?)
G Em
Look for your infor - mation,
G Em F
Yes there's one thing, the one thing that still holds true,

(What's that?)

Chorus 2 As Chorus 1

Instrumental | Am | G | Em | F |

| Am | G | Em ||

F   G
Whoa, whoa, whoa, whoa.

Chorus 3

F   G   Am
  (That's the look, that's the look,)

            G F
The look of love.

            G   Am
(That's the look, that's the look,)

            G F
The look of love.

            G   Am
(That's the look, that's the look,)

            G F   G   Am   G Am
The look of love.___ (Look of love.)

Verse 3

F/A   G/A   Em/A   F/A
If you judge a book by the cover,

                        G/A   Em/A   F/A
Then you judge the look by the lover.

                    G/A   Em/A   F/A
I hope you'll soon re - cover,

              G/A   Em/A   F/A
Me, I go from one ex - treme to an - other.

Bridge

F   G   Am
   And though my friends just might ask me,

                G   F   G   Am G F
They say, "Martin, maybe one day you'll find true love."

Em F   G Am
I___ say, "Maybe,   but there must be a solution

G   F   G   Am   G   F   Em
To the one thing, the one thing   we can't find."

Chorus 4

```
F                   G                    Am
   (That's the look, that's the look,)
          G    F
Sisters and brothers
                 G                    Am
(That's the look, that's the look,)
                G         F
Should help___ each other,
                 G                    Am
(That's the look, that's the look,)
         G     F     G  Am
Ooh, ooh, ooh,      Heavens above.
F                   G                    Am
   (That's the look, that's the look,)
           G           F
Hip hip    hooray,___
                                      Am
(That's the look, that's the look,)
                          G F
Yippee-i yippee - i   ay,
                 G                    Am
(That's the look, that's the look,)
               G  F      G
(Be lucky in  love),___
Am        G   Am
   Look of  love.
```

Love Really Hurts Without You

Words & Music by Ben Findon & Les Charles

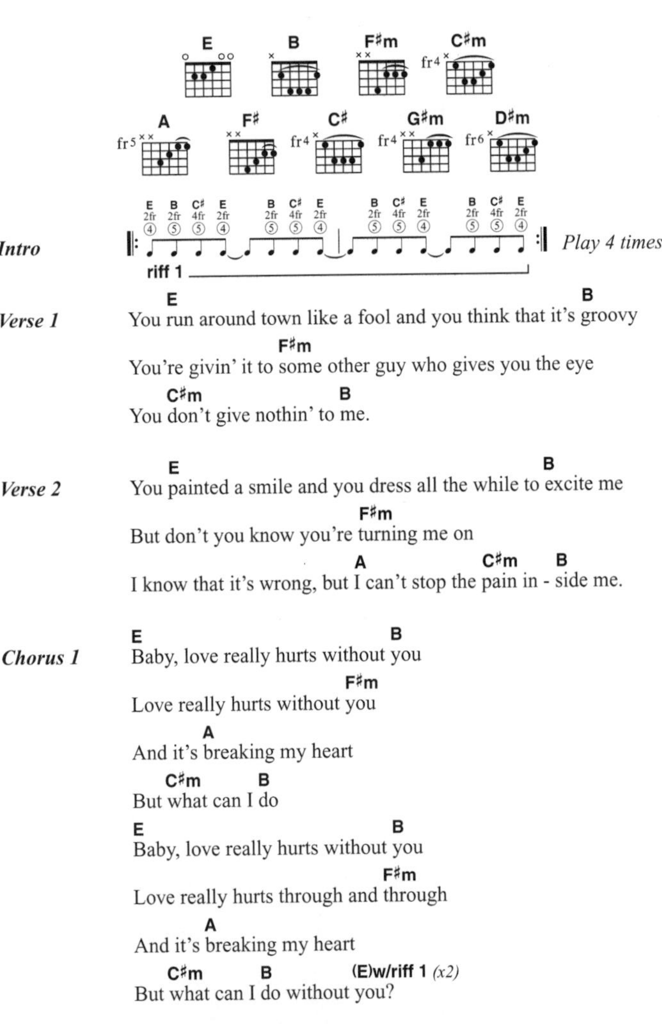

Intro — riff 1 — *Play 4 times*

Verse 1

E B
You run around town like a fool and you think that it's groovy
F♯m
You're givin' it to some other guy who gives you the eye
C♯m B
You don't give nothin' to me.

Verse 2

E B
You painted a smile and you dress all the while to excite me
F♯m
But don't you know you're turning me on
A C♯m B
I know that it's wrong, but I can't stop the pain in - side me.

Chorus 1

E B
Baby, love really hurts without you
F♯m
Love really hurts without you
A
And it's breaking my heart
C♯m B
But what can I do
E B
Baby, love really hurts without you
F♯m
Love really hurts through and through
A
And it's breaking my heart
C♯m B (E)w/riff 1 *(x2)*
But what can I do without you?

Verse 3

```
    E                                                             B
You walk like a dream and you make like you're Queen of the action
                            F♯m
You're using every trick in the book the way that you look
      C♯m               B
You're really something to see.
```

Verse 4

```
    E                                                B
You cheat and you lie to impress any guy that you fancy
                                F♯m
But don't you know I'm out of my mind, so give me a sign
    A               C♯m   B
And help to ease the pain in - side me.
```

Chorus 2

```
E                                B
Baby, love really hurts without you
                             F♯m
Love really hurts without you
          A
And it's breaking my heart
     C♯m       B
But what can I do
E                                B
Baby, love really hurts without you
                                    F♯m
Love really hurts through and through
          A
And it's breaking my heart
     C♯m       B             (E)w/riff 1 (x2)   (F♯)w/riff 1 (up 1 tone)
But what can I do without you?
```

Chorus 3

```
   F♯                                C♯
|: Baby, love really hurts without you
                             G♯m
Love really hurts without you
          B
And it's breaking my heart
     D♯m       C♯
But what can I do
F♯                               C♯
Baby, love really hurts without you
                                    G♯m
Love really hurts through and through
          B
And it's breaking my heart
     D♯m       C♯
But what can I do? :|  Repeat to fade
```

Lucky Man

Words & Music by Richard Ashcroft

G D Dsus2 Asus2 Em7 A

Intro |: G | D Dsus2 | Asus2 | Asus2 :| *Play 8 times*

Verse 1

G D Dsus2
Happiness, more or less,
Asus2
It's just a change in me, something in my liberty.
G D Dsus2 Asus2
Oh,___ my, my.______
G D Dsus2
Happiness, coming and going,
Asus2
I watch you look at me, watch my fever growing,
G D Dsus2 Asus2
I know just where I am.______

Pre-chorus 1

Em7
But how many corners do I have to turn?
G
How many times do I have to learn
D A
All the love I have is in my mind?

Chorus 1

(A) G D Dsus2 Asus2
Well, I'm a lucky man____________
G D Dsus2 Asus2
With fire in my hands.____________

Verse 2

G D Dsus2
Happiness, something in my own place,
Asus2 G
I'm stood here naked, smiling, I feel no dis - grace
D Dsus2 Asus2
With who I am.______
G D Dsus2
Happiness, coming and going,
Asus2
I watch you look at me, watch my fever growing,
G D Dsus2 Asus2
I know just who I am.______

Pre-chorus 2 As Pre-chorus 1

Chorus 2

(A) G D Dsus2 Asus2
I hope you understand.______________
G D Dsus2 Asus2
I hope you understand.______________

Interlude

(Asus2) G D Dsus2 Asus2
Oh,_______________ yeah.
G
You know, you know, you know, you know, you know,
D Dsus2
You know, you know, you know.
Asus2
Gotta love that'll never die, no, no.

Verse 3

G D Dsus2
Happiness, more or less,
Asus2
It's just a change in me, something in my liberty.
G D Dsus2
Happiness, coming and going,
Asus2
I watch you look at me, watch my fever growing,
G D Dsus2 Asus2 G
I know, oh,___ my, my.________

cont.

```
     D       Dsus2     Asus2  G
Oh,___ my,        my.________
     D       Dsus2     Asus2  G
Oh,___ my,        my.________
     D       Dsus2     Asus2
Oh,___ my,        my.______
      G                    D      Dsus2  Asus2
Gotta love that'll never die.____________
        G                   D      Dsus2    Asus2
I gotta love that'll never die, no,         no.
```

Outro

```
(Asus2)  G            D        Dsus2  Asus2       G  D  Dsus2
Oh, I'm a lucky man.________________
Asus2                                                 G  D  Dsus2
   It's just a change in me, something in my liberty.
Asus2                                                 G  D  Dsus2
   It's just a change in me, something in my liberty.
Asus2
   It's just a change in me, something in my liberty.
G        D    Dsus2   Asus2
   Oh,___ my,    my.______
G        D    Dsus2   Asus2
   Oh,___ my,    my.

It's just a change in me, something in my liberty.
G        D    Dsus2   Asus2
   Oh,___ my,    my.______
G        D    Dsus2   Asus2    G    D  Dsus2  Asus2
   Oh,___ my,    my.______
```

Me And Bobby McGee

Words & Music by Kris Kristofferson & Fred Foster

G C/G D C D7 A E

Intro | G | C/G | G C/G | G ||

Verse 1

G
Busted flat in Baton Rouge, waiting for a train
D
And I's feeling nearly as faded as my jeans.

Bobby thumbed a diesel down just before it rained,
G C/G
It rode us all the way to New Or - leans.
G
I pulled my harpoon out of my dirty red bandana,
C
I was playing soft while Bobby sang the blues.
G
Windshield wipers slapping time, I was holding Bobby's hand in mine,
D
We sang every song that driver knew.

Chorus 1

C G
Freedom's just another word for nothing left to lose,
D7 G
Nothing, don't mean nothing, honey, if it ain't free, now now.
C G
And feeling good was easy, Lord,___ when he sang the blues,
D7
You know feeling good was good enough for me,
G
Good enough for me and my Bobby Mc - Gee.

Verse 2

```
A
  From the Kentucky coal mines to the California sun,
                                E
Hey, Bobby shared the secrets of my soul.
Through all kinds of weather, through everything that we done,
                                 A
Hey, Bobby baby kept me from the cold.
One day up near Salinas, Lord, I let him slip away,
                                         D
He's looking for that home and I hope he finds it,
                                         A
But I'd trade all of my tomorrows for one single yesterday
        E
To be holding Bobby's body next to mine.
```

Chorus 2

```
D                              A
Freedom's just another word for  nothing left to lose,
E                                A
Nothing, that's all that Bobby left  me, yeah.
   D                               A
But feeling good was easy, Lord,___ when he sang the blues,
    E
Hey, feeling good was good enough for me, hmm hmm,
                                         A
Good enough for me and my Bobby Mc - Gee.
```

Verse 3

```
A
La la la, la la la la, la la la, la la la la
                        E
La la la la la Bobby Mc - Gee.
La la la la la, la la la la la
                          A
La la la la la, Bobby Mc - Gee, la.
La la la, la la la la la la,
                                                               E
La la la la la la la la la, hey now Bobby now, Bobby Mc - Gee yeah.
Na na na na na na na na, na na na na na na na na na na na
                              A
Hey now Bobby now, Bobby Mc - Gee, yeah.
```

Verse 4

```
A
Lord, I'm calling my lover, calling my man,

I said I'm calling my lover just the best I can,
                                                      E
C'mon, where is Bobby now, where is Bobby Mc - Gee, yeah.

Lordy, Lordy, Lordy, Lordy, Lordy, Lordy, Lordy, Lord.
                           A
Hey, hey, hey, Bobby Mc - Gee, Lord.
```

Instrumental

```
|: A   | A   | A   | A   |
 | A   | A   | E   | E   |
 | E   | E   | E   | E   |
 | E   | E   | A   | A   :|
|: A   | A   | A   | A   |
 | A   | A   | E   | E   :|
```

Outro

```
E
Lordy, Lordy, Lordy, Lordy, Lordy, Lordy, Lordy, Lord.
                           A
Hey, hey, hey, Bobby Mc - Gee.
```

Miss You

Words & Music by Mick Jagger & Keith Richards

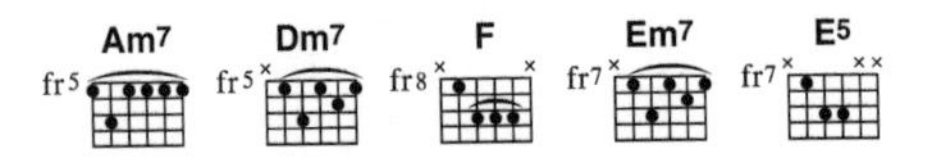

Intro ‖: Am7 | Am7 | Dm7 | Dm7 :‖ *Play 3 times*

Verse 1

```
(Dm7)      Am7
I've been holding out so long,

I've been sleeping all alone,
         Dm7
Lord I miss you.
            Am7
I've been hanging on the phone,

I've been sleeping all alone,
            Dm7
I want to kiss you.
```

Link 1

```
(Dm7) Am7
Ooh   ooh ooh, ooh ooh ooh,
            Dm7
Ooh ooh ooh, ooh.
       Am7
Ooh ooh ooh, ooh ooh ooh,
            Dm7
Ooh ooh ooh, ooh.
```

```
            (Dm7)              Am7
Verse 2     Well, I've been haunted in my sleep,

            You've been starring in my dreams,
                    Dm7
            Lord I miss you, child.
                        Am7
            I've been waiting in the hall,

            Been waiting on your call.
                        Dm7
            When the phone rings

            It's just some friends of mine that say,
                   Am7
            "Hey,      what's the matter man?

            We're gonna come around at twelve
                                            Dm7
            With some Puerto Rican girls that are just dyin' to meet you.
                          Am7
            We're gonna bring a case of wine,

            Hey, let's go mess and fool around
                  Dm7
            You know, like we used to."


            (Dm7) Am7
Link 2      Ah ah ah, ah ah ah,
                  Dm7
            Ah ah ah, ah.
                  Am7
            Ah ah ah, ah ah ah,
                  Dm7
            Ah ah ah, ah.


            F   Em7                  Dm7
Bridge      Oh, everybody waits so long.
            F   Em7                     Dm7
            Oh, baby why you wait so long?
                          E5
            Won't you       come on, come on.


Link 3      | Am7    | Am7    | Dm7    | Dm7    ||
```

Verse 3

(Dm7) Am7
I've been walking Central Park,

Singing after dark,

Dm7
People think I'm crazy.

Am7
I've been stumbling on my feet,

Shuffling through the street,

Dm7
Asking people, "What's the matter with you boy?"

Am7 Dm7
Sometimes I want to say to my - self,

Sometimes I say,...

Link 4

(Dm7) Am7
Ooh ooh ooh, ooh ooh ooh,

Dm7
Ooh ooh ooh, ooh.

Am7
Ooh ooh ooh, ooh ooh ooh,

Dm7
I won't miss you child.

Instrumental 𝄆 Am7 | Am7 | Dm7 | Dm7 𝄇

Verse 4

(Dm7) Am7
I guess I'm lying to myself,

It's just you and no one else,

Dm7
Lord, I won't kiss you child.

Am7
You've just been blotting out my mind,

Fooling on my time,

Dm7
No, I won't miss you, baby, yeah.

Am7
Lord, I miss you child.

Dm7
Ooh.___

Link 5

(Dm7) Am7
Ah ah ah, ah ah ah,
Dm7
Ah ah ah, ah.

Lord, I miss you child.
Am7
Ah ah ah, ah ah ah,
Dm7
Ah ah ah, ah.

Lord, I miss you child.
Am7
Ah ah ah, ah ah ah,
Dm7
Ah ah ah, ah.

Outro

|: Am7 | Am7 | Dm7 | Dm7 :| *Repeat and fade*

Money (That's What I Want)

Words & Music by Berry Gordy & Janie Bradford

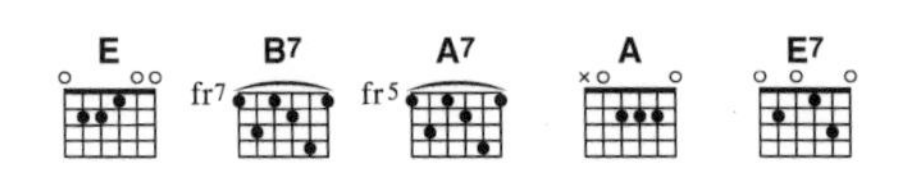

Intro | E | E | E | E |

| B7 | A7 | E | B7 ||

Verse 1

```
E                                     A  E
   The best things in life are free,

But you can keep 'em for the birds and bees.
                  A7
Now, give me money, (That's what I want.)
                  E7
That's what I want, (That's what I want.)
                  B7     A7
That's what I want,___ yeah,
E                          B7
   That's what I want.
```

Verse 2

```
E                                     A  E
   Your loving give me a thrill,

But your loving don't pay my bills.
                  A7
Now, give me money, (That's what I want.)
                  E7
That's what I want, (That's what I want.)
                  B7     A7
That's what I want,___ yeah,
E                          B7
   That's what I want.
```

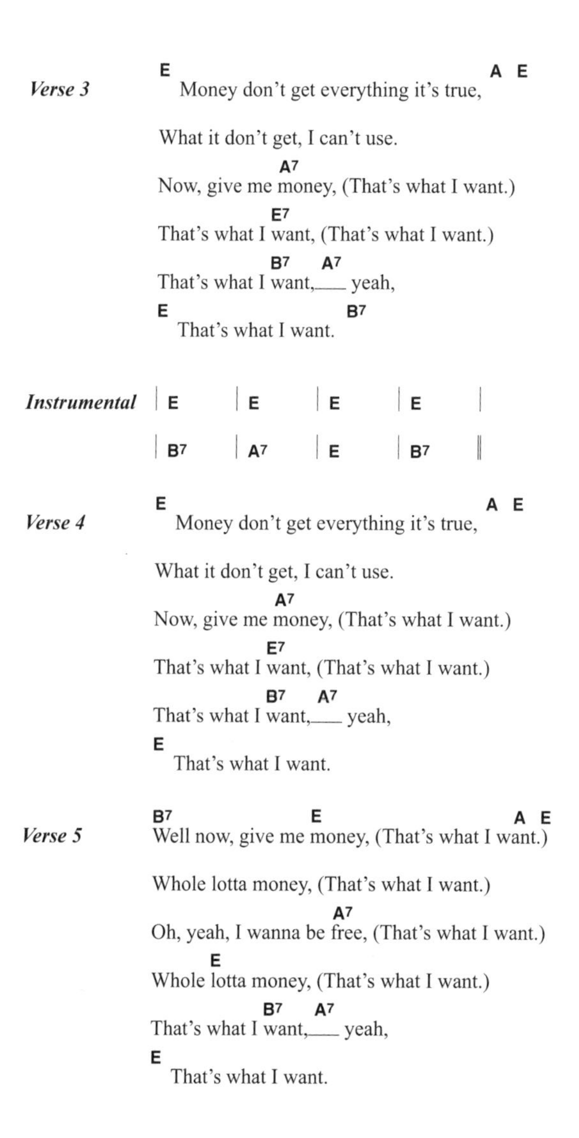
Verse 3
E A E
Money don't get everything it's true,
What it don't get, I can't use.
A7
Now, give me money, (That's what I want.)
E7
That's what I want, (That's what I want.)
B7 A7
That's what I want,___ yeah,
E B7
That's what I want.
Instrumental
| E | E | E | E |
| B7 | A7 | E | B7 ||
Verse 4
E A E
Money don't get everything it's true,
What it don't get, I can't use.
A7
Now, give me money, (That's what I want.)
E7
That's what I want, (That's what I want.)
B7 A7
That's what I want,___ yeah,
E
That's what I want.
Verse 5
B7 E A E
Well now, give me money, (That's what I want.)
Whole lotta money, (That's what I want.)
A7
Oh, yeah, I wanna be free, (That's what I want.)
E
Whole lotta money, (That's what I want.)
B7 A7
That's what I want,___ yeah,
E
That's what I want.

Verse 6

B7 E
Well now, give me money, (That's what I want.)

Whole lotta money, (That's what I want.)

A7
Whoa yeah, you know I need money, (That's what I want.)

E
Oh, now give me money, that's what I want,

B7 A7
That's what I want,___ yeah,

E E7
That's what I want.

The Night

Words & Music by Robert Gaudio & Al Ruzicka

Intro ‖: A♭ | Gm | G/B | Cm :‖

A♭ Gm G/B Cm
Be - ware of his promise,

A♭ Gm G/B Cm
Be - lieve what I say.

A♭ Gm G/B Cm
Be - fore I go for - ever,

A♭ Gm G/B Cm
Be sure of what you say.

Verse 1

(Cm) Fm B♭
So he paints a pretty picture

G Cm
And he tells you that he needs you.

Fm B♭
And he covers you with flowers,

G Cm
And he always keeps you dreaming.

Fm B♭
If he always keeps you dreaming,

G Cm
You won't have a lonely hour.

Fm B♭
If a day could last for - ever,

G Cm
You might like your ivory tower.

Chorus 1

(Cm) A♭ E♭/G B♭
But the night begins to turn your head a - round,

A♭ E♭/G B♭
And you know you're gonna lose more than you've found.

A♭ E♭/G (B♭)
Yes, the night begins to turn your head a - round.

Link 1

| B♭ | B♭ | B♭m | B♭m ||

Bridge

A♭ Gm G/B Cm
Be - ware of his promise,

A♭ Gm G/B Cm
Be - lieve what I say.

A♭ Gm G/B Cm
Be - fore I go for - ever,

A♭ Gm G/B Cm
Be sure of what you say.

Verse 2

(Cm) Fm B♭
For the words become too easy,

G Cm
If you don't believe I'm leaving.

Fm B♭
And good - bye may come too quickly,

G Cm
If you really think he loves you.

Fm B♭
If you really think he loves you,

G Cm
You would give your love so sweetly.

Fm B♭
If the day could last for - ever,

G Cm
You would fall in love com - pletely.

Chorus 2 As Chorus 1

Link 2 As Link 1

Instrumental ‖: **A♭** | **Gm** | **G/B** | **Cm** :‖

Chorus 3

```
(Cm)     A♭                          E♭/G    B♭
And the night begins to turn your head a - round,
         A♭                          E♭/G               B♭
And you know you're gonna lose more than you've found.
         A♭                          E♭/G    B♭
Yes, the night begins to turn your head a - round,
         A♭                          E♭/G               B♭
And you know you're gonna lose more than you've found.
         A♭                          E♭/G    B♭
Yes, the night begins to turn your head a - round.    To fade
```

Movin' On Up

Words & Music by Bobby Gillespie, Robert Young & Andrew Innes

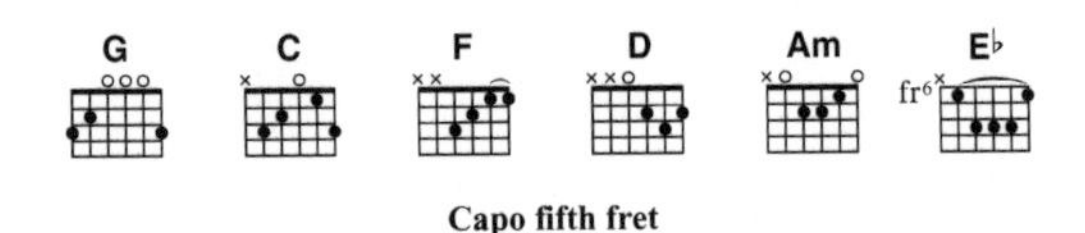

Capo fifth fret

Intro ‖: G | G C F C | G | G C F C :‖ G | G C F C |

Verse 1

```
GCFC  G     C   FC  G
    I was blind, now I can see,
C   F      C  G     CF  C G
You made a believer,  out of me.
CFC  D     G    D     C
  I was blind, now I can see,
C   F      C  G      CF   C G
You made a believer,  out of me.
```

Chorus 1

```
     C  F  C    D
I'm movin' on up    now,
                    C
Gettin' out of the darkness.
                  Am
My light shines on,
                  C
My light shines on,
                  G      | G C F C |
My light shines on.
```

Verse 2

```
GCFC  G   CF   C  G
    I was lost,  now I'm found,
C  F    CG   C     F  C G
I believe in you,  I've got no bounds.
CFC  D   GD       C
  I was lost,  now I'm found,
F   C      G   C  F  C G
I  believe in you,  I got no bounds.
```

```
                                   D           G  D
Chorus 2      I'm movin' on up   now,
                         G  D  C          F  C
              Gettin' out of the darkness.
                         F  C   Am
              My light shines on,
                                C
              My light shines on,
                         F  C   G      | G C F C |
              My light shines on,
              C               F  C   G      | G C F C |
                 My light shines on,
              C               F  C   G
                 My light shines on.

Instrumental  ||: G   | G   | F   | F   | E♭  | E♭  | C   | C   :||

              ||: G   | G C F C | G    | G C F C :||

                  G                   F
Outro         ||:    My light shines on,
              E♭                    C
                 My light shines on.        :||

                    G
              ||:  I'm getting outta darkness,
                  F
              My light shines on.
                  E♭
              I'm getting outta darkness,
                     C
              Your light shines on.       :||        Repeat to fade
```

Mr. Blue Sky

Words & Music by Jeff Lynne

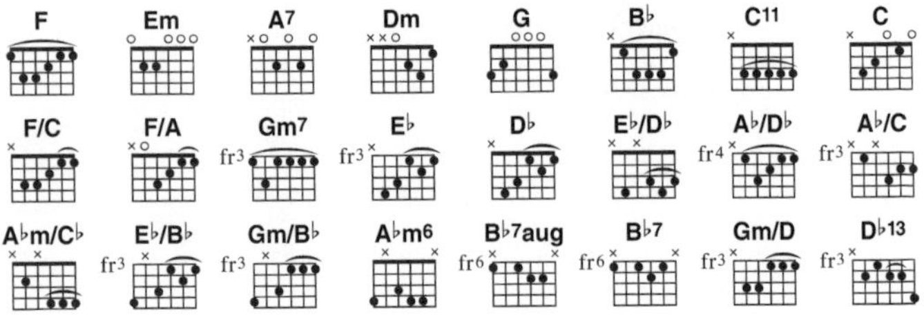

F Em A7 Dm G B♭ C11 C
F/C F/A Gm7 E♭ D♭ E♭/D♭ A♭/D♭ A♭/C
A♭m/C♭ E♭/B♭ Gm/B♭ A♭m6 B♭7aug B♭7 Gm/D D♭13

Intro *(spoken)* | F | F | F |
Morning! Today's forecast calls for blue skies.
‖: F | F | F | F :‖

Verse 1

F
The sun is shining in the sky,
Em A7 Dm
There ain't a cloud in sight.
G Em A7
It's stopped raining, every - body's in a play
B♭ C11 F C
And don't you know, it's a beautiful new day, hey.___

Verse 2

F
Running down the avenue,
Em A7 Dm
See how the sun shines brightly.
G Em A7
In the city, on the streets where once was pity,
B♭ C11 F C
Mister Blue Sky is living here to - day, hey.___

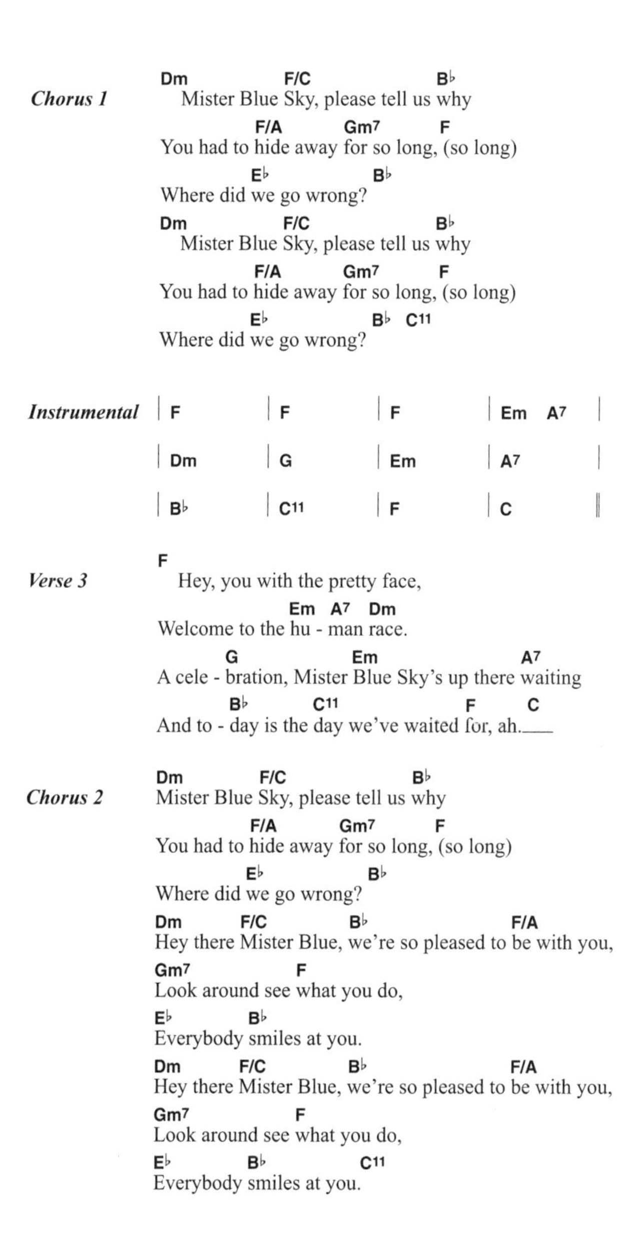
Chorus 1
Dm F/C B♭
Mister Blue Sky, please tell us why
F/A Gm7 F
You had to hide away for so long, (so long)
E♭ B♭
Where did we go wrong?
Dm F/C B♭
Mister Blue Sky, please tell us why
F/A Gm7 F
You had to hide away for so long, (so long)
E♭ B♭ C11
Where did we go wrong?
Instrumental
F	F	F	Em A7
Dm	G	Em	A7
B♭	C11	F	C	
Verse 3
F
Hey, you with the pretty face,
Em A7 Dm
Welcome to the hu - man race.
G Em A7
A cele - bration, Mister Blue Sky's up there waiting
B♭ C11 F C
And to - day is the day we've waited for, ah.
Chorus 2
Dm F/C B♭
Mister Blue Sky, please tell us why
F/A Gm7 F
You had to hide away for so long, (so long)
E♭ B♭
Where did we go wrong?
Dm F/C B♭ F/A
Hey there Mister Blue, we're so pleased to be with you,
Gm7 F
Look around see what you do,
E♭ B♭
Everybody smiles at you.
Dm F/C B♭ F/A
Hey there Mister Blue, we're so pleased to be with you,
Gm7 F
Look around see what you do,
E♭ B♭ C11
Everybody smiles at you.

Interlude 1

```
F
Mister Blue Sky.
Em    A7 Dm   G
Mis - ter Blue Sky.
Em  A7        B♭   C11  F  C
     Mister Blue Sky.___
```

Verse 4

```
F
Mister Blue, you did it right
                      Em    A7 Dm
But soon comes Mis - ter Night
           G                  Em                A7
Creepin' over, now his hand is on your shoulder.
          B♭                C11
Never mind, I'll re - member you this,
D♭            E♭                   Dm
   I'll re - member you this way.
```

Chorus 3

```
Dm                F/C                       B♭
Mister Blue Sky, please tell us why
                 F/A         Gm7          F
You had to hide away for so long,  (so long)
                 E♭           B♭
Where did we go wrong?
Dm            F/C              B♭                        F/A
Hey there Mister Blue, we're so pleased to be with you,
Gm7                   F
Look around see what you do,
E♭              B♭
Everybody smiles at you.
```

Interlude 2

```
Dm          F/C
   Ba da,     da ba da ba,
B♭           F/A
   Ba da,     da ba da ba,
Gm7         F                    E♭  B♭
   Ba da,     da ba da ba, da, da.
Dm          F/C
   Ba da,     da ba da ba,
B♭           F/A
   Ba da,     da ba da ba,
Gm7         F
   Ba da,     da ba da ba,
E♭  B♭  F
Da, da, da.
```

Outro | D♭ | D♭ | D♭ | D♭ | D♭ |

D♭ E♭/D♭ D♭
Ah,___

E♭/D♭ D♭ E♭/D♭ A♭/D♭
Ah, ah, ah, ah.

E♭/D♭ D♭
Ah,___

E♭/D♭ D♭ E♭/D♭ A♭/C A♭m/C♭
Ah, ah, ah, ah.

| E♭/B♭ | Gm/B♭ | A♭m6 | B♭7aug B♭7 |

| E♭ | Gm/D | D♭13 | D♭13 |

| E♭ | E♭ | E♭ | E♭ ||
Mister Blue Sky.

My Baby Just Cares For Me
from WHOOPEE!

Words by Gus Kahn

Music by Walter Donaldson

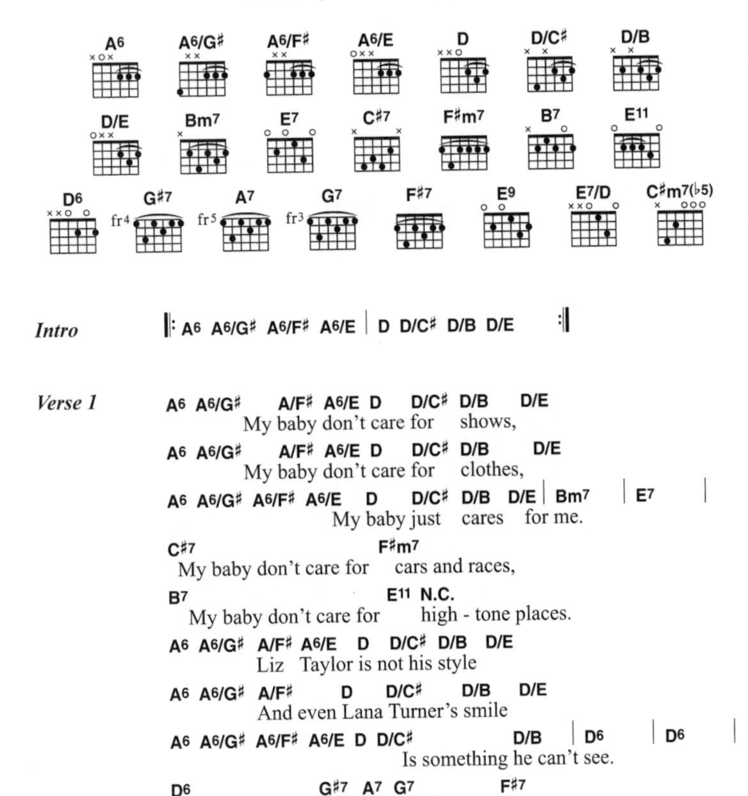

Intro

|: A6 A6/G♯ A6/F♯ A6/E | D D/C♯ D/B D/E :|

Verse 1

```
A6  A6/G♯        A/F♯  A6/E  D     D/C♯  D/B     D/E
                 My baby don't care for    shows,
A6  A6/G♯        A/F♯  A6/E  D     D/C♯  D/B     D/E
                 My baby don't care for    clothes,
A6  A6/G♯  A6/F♯  A6/E   D     D/C♯  D/B  D/E | Bm7  | E7  |
                  My baby just    cares   for me.
C♯7                           F♯m7
 My baby don't care for        cars and races,
B7                            E11  N.C.
  My baby don't care for        high - tone places.
A6  A6/G♯  A/F♯  A6/E  D  D/C♯  D/B  D/E
           Liz   Taylor is not his style
A6  A6/G♯  A/F♯        D     D/C♯       D/B    D/E
           And even Lana Turner's smile
A6  A6/G♯  A6/F♯  A6/E  D  D/C♯          D/B  | D6   | D6  |
                          Is something he can't see.
D6                  G♯7  A7  G7         F♯7
 My baby don't care___  who knows,___
Bm7               E9      (A6)
 My baby just cares for me.
```

Link

| A6 A6/G♯ A6/F♯ A6/E | D D/C♯ D/B E11 ||

Piano solo

```
| A6 A6/G# A6/F# A6/E | D D/C# D/B E11     |
| A6 A6/G# A6/F# A6/E | D D/C# D/B D/E     |
| A6        | A6        | Bm7       | E7        |
| C#7       | C#7       | F#m7      | F#m7      |
| B7        | B7        | E11       | N.C.  E11 |
| A6 A6/G# A6/F# A6/E | D D/C# D/B E11     |
| A6 A6/G# A6/F# A6/E | D D/C# D/B D/E     |
| A6        | A6        | D6        | D6        |
| D6        | G#7       | A7   G7   | F#7       |
| Bm7       | E9        | A6  F#m7  | Bm7  E7   ||
```

Verse 2

```
A6 A6/G# A6/F#  A6/E D D/C#  D/B        D/E A6         A6/G#
                  Ba - by,        my baby don't care for shows
A6/F# A6/E       D     D/C# D/B D/E
          And he don't even care for clothes,
A6 A6/G# A6/F# A6/E D D/C#  D/B D/E Bm7     E7
                           He cares         for me.
C#7                     F#m7
  My baby don't care___ for cars and races,
B7                     E11 N.C.
  Baby don't care for,     he don't care for high - tone places.
A6 A6/G# A6/F# A6/E D  D/C# D/B   D/E
Liz___  Taylor is    not his   style
A6 A6/G#    A6/F# A6/E  D  D/C# D/B  D/E
       And even  Libe - ra - ce's  smile
A6 A6/G# A6/F# A6/E  D       D/C# D/B    D/E   D6
                      Is some - thing___ he can't see,

Is something he can't see.
                     G#7     A7      G7  F#7
I wonder what's wrong___ with ba - by?
Bm7                E9        E7/D
  My baby just cares for,
C#m7(b5)           F#7
  My baby just cares for,
Bm7                E7       A6
  My baby just cares for me.
```

My Girl

Words & Music by Michael Barson

C♯m A F♯m G♯m B
E B/D♯ A/E E/B E/G♯

Intro | 𝄆 C♯m | (C♯m) | A | F♯m | G♯m B 𝄇 |

Verse 1

C♯m A
My girl's mad at me,
C♯m F♯m
I didn't wanna see the film tonight.
C♯m A
I found it hard to say,
C♯m F♯m
She thought I'd had e - nough of her.

Bridge 1

E B/D♯ C♯m F♯m A/E B/D♯
Why can't she see she's lovely to me?
E B/D♯ C♯m E/B A
But I like to stay in and watch T. - V.
E/G♯ F♯m A/E B
On my own every now and then.

Verse 2

C♯m A
My girl's mad at me,
C♯m F♯m
Been on the tele - phone for an hour.
C♯m A
We hardly said a word,
C♯m F♯m
I tried and tried but I could not be heard.

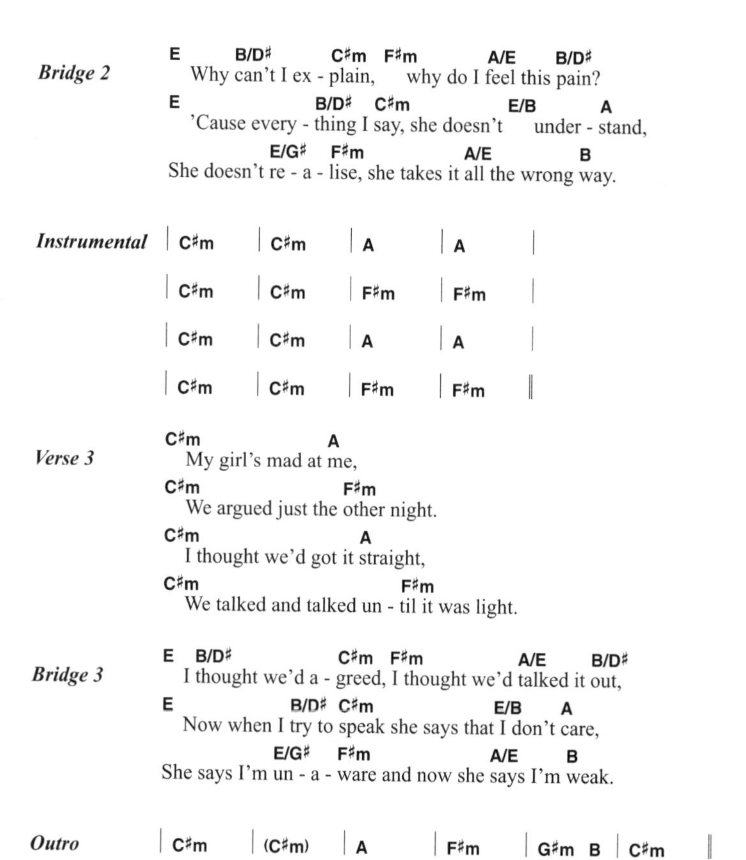
Bridge 2
E B/D♯ C♯m F♯m A/E B/D♯
Why can't I ex - plain, why do I feel this pain?
E B/D♯ C♯m E/B A
'Cause every - thing I say, she doesn't under - stand,
E/G♯ F♯m A/E B
She doesn't re - a - lise, she takes it all the wrong way.
Instrumental
C♯m C♯m A A
C♯m C♯m F♯m F♯m
C♯m C♯m A A
C♯m C♯m F♯m F♯m
Verse 3
C♯m A
My girl's mad at me,
C♯m F♯m
We argued just the other night.
C♯m A
I thought we'd got it straight,
C♯m F♯m
We talked and talked un - til it was light.
Bridge 3
E B/D♯ C♯m F♯m A/E B/D♯
I thought we'd a - greed, I thought we'd talked it out,
E B/D♯ C♯m E/B A
Now when I try to speak she says that I don't care,
E/G♯ F♯m A/E B
She says I'm un - a - ware and now she says I'm weak.
Outro
C♯m (C♯m) A F♯m G♯m B C♯m

Perfect Day

Words & Music by Lou Reed

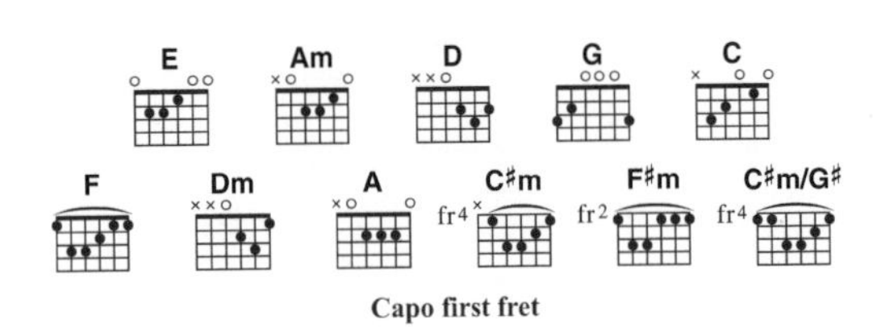

Capo first fret

Intro | E Am | E Am ||

Verse 1

Am D
Just a perfect day,
G C
Drink sangria in the park,
F Dm
And then later, when it gets dark,
E
We go home.
Am D
Just a perfect day,
G C
Feed animals in the zoo,
F Dm
Then later, a movie too,
E
And then home.

Chorus 1

A D
Oh, it's such a perfect day,
C♯m D
I'm glad I spent it with you.
A E
Oh, such a perfect day,
F♯m E D
You just keep me hanging on,
F♯m E D
You just keep me hanging on.

Verse 2

Am D
Just a perfect day,
G C
Problems all left alone,
F Dm
Weekenders on our own,
E
It's such fun.
Am D
Just a perfect day,
G C
You made me for - get myself,
F Dm
I thought I was someone else,
E
Someone good.

Chorus 2

A D
Oh, it's such a perfect day,
C♯m D
I'm glad I spent it with you.
A E
Oh, such a perfect day,
F♯m E D
You just keep me hanging on,
F♯m E D
You just keep me hanging on.

Piano Solo

F♯m	E	D
F♯m	E	D
F♯m	E	D	

Outro

C♯m/G♯ G D A
You're going to reap just what you sow,
C♯m/G♯ G D A
You're going to reap just what you sow,
C♯m/G♯ G D A
You're going to reap just what you sow,
C♯m/G♯ G D
You're going to reap just what you sow.__

||: A | F♯m | E | D :|| A ||

Please Mr. Postman

Words & Music by Brian Holland, Freddie Gorman,
Robert Bateman, Georgia Dobbins & William Garrett

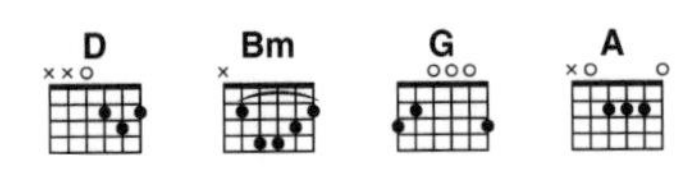

Intro

D
(Wait), oh yes, wait a minute Mr. Postman,
Bm
(Wait,) wait Mr. Postman.

Chorus 1

D Bm
(Please Mister Postman, look and see,) whoa yeah,

(Is there a letter in your bag for me,)
G
Please, please Mr. Postman,
A
(Must have been a mighty long time,) whoa yeah,

(Since I've heard from this boyfriend of mine.)

Verse 1

D
There must be some word today
Bm
From my boyfriend so far away,
G
Please Mr. Postman look and see,
A
Is there a letter, a letter for me?

Verse 2

D
I've been standing here waiting Mr. Postman,
Bm
So, so patiently
G
For just a card or just a letter
A
Saying he's returning home to me.

Chorus 2

(A) D
Please Mr. Postman.

Bm
(Please Mister Postman, look and see,) whoa yeah,

(Is there a letter in your bag for me,)

G
Please, please Mr. Postman,

A
(Must have been a mighty long time,) whoa yeah,

(Since I've heard from this boyfriend of mine.)

Verse 3

D
So many days you passed me by,

Bm
You saw the tears standing in my eye.

G
You wouldn't stop to make me feel better,

A
By leaving me a card or a letter.

Chorus 3

(A) D
Please Mr. Postman look and see,

Bm
Is there a letter, oh yeah, in your bag for me,

G
You know it's been so long,

A
Yes, since I heard from this boyfriend of mine.

Chorus 4

(A) D
You better wait a minute, wait a minute,

Bm
Oh, you better wait a minute,

G
Please, please Mr. Postman,

A
Please check and see, just one more time for me.

Chorus 5

```
(A)        D
You better wait, wait a minute,
                  Bm
Wait a minute, wait a minute, wait a minute,
              G
Please Mr. Postman,
   A
De - liver the letter, the sooner the better.
```

Chorus 6

```
D
Wait a minute, wait a minute,
                  Bm
Wait a minute, please Mr. Postman, wait,
                  G
Wait a minute, wait a minute.
              A
Whoa, oh.        To fade
```

Rolling In The Deep

Words & Music by Paul Epworth & Adele Adkins

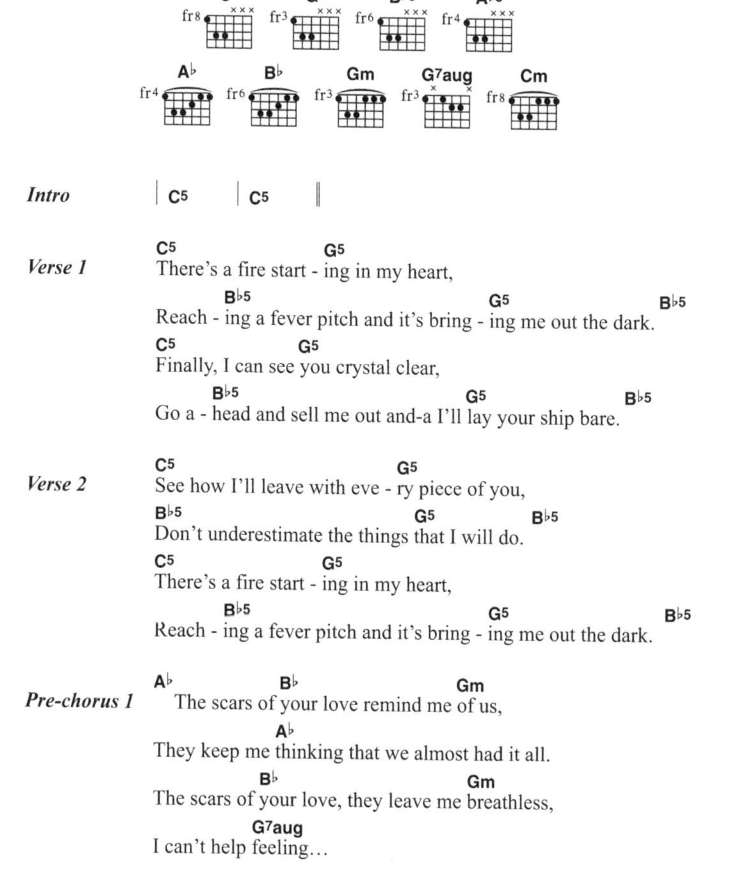

Chorus 1

(G7aug)   Cm B♭
We could have had it all,___

                  A♭
Rolling in the deep.

    B♭   Cm   B♭
You had my heart in - side your hand

          A♭   B♭
And you played it to the beat.

Verse 3

C5   G5
Baby, I have no sto - ry to be told,

          B♭5   G5   B♭5
But I've heard one on you and I'm gonna make your head burn.

C5   G5
Think of me in the depths of your despair,

        B♭5   G5   B♭5
Make a home down there as mine sure won't be shared.

Pre-chorus 2 As Pre-chorus 1

Chorus 2 As Chorus 1

Bridge

B♭   A♭ B♭
Could have had it all,___

                  Cm   B♭
Rolling in the deep.___

                             A♭
You had my heart in - side your hand,

          B♭
But you played it with a beating.

Verse 4

N.C.(Cm)
Throw your soul through every open door,

Count your blessings to find what you look for.

Cm
Turn my sorrow into treasured gold,

You'll pay me back in kind and reap just what you've sown.

```
              Cm                            B♭
Breakdown     (You're gonna wish you never had met me),
Chorus 3
                                      A♭
              We could have had it all,
                 B♭                   Cm  B♭
              We could have had it all,___
                A♭
              It all, it all, it all.

                                      Cm  B♭
Chorus 4      We could have had it all,___
                               A♭
              Rolling in the deep.
                 B♭                   Cm      B♭
              You had my heart in - side your hand
                         A♭
              And you played it to the beat.
              B♭                  Cm  B♭
              Could have had it all,___
                               A♭
              Rolling in the deep.
                 B♭                   Cm      B♭
              You had my heart in - side your hand,
                        A♭
              But you played it, you played it, you played it,
                 B♭                Cm
              You played it to the beat.
```

Rehab

Words & Music by Amy Winehouse

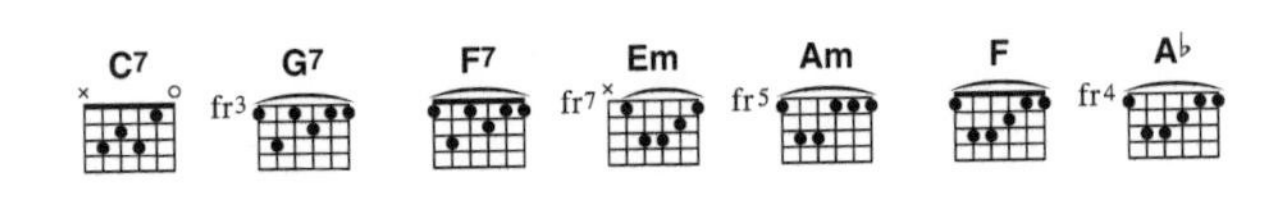

Chorus 1

C7
They tried to make me go to rehab, I said, "No, no, no."

Yes, I've been black but when I come back you'll know, know, know.

G7 F7
I ain't got the time and if my daddy thinks I'm fine,

C7 F7 C7
He's tried to make me go to rehab, I won't go, go, go.

Verse 1

Em Am
I'd rather be at home___ with Ray,

F A♭
I ain't got seventeen days.

Em Am
'Cause there's nothing, there's nothing you can teach me

F A♭
That I can't learn from Mr. Hathaway.

G7
I didn't get a lot in class,

F7
But I know we don't come in a shot glass.

Chorus 2

C7
They tried to make me go to rehab, I said, "No, no, no."

Yes, I've been black but when I come back you'll know, know, know.

G7 F7
I ain't got the time and if my daddy thinks I'm fine,

C7 F7 C7
He's tried to make me go to rehab, I won't go, go, go.

Verse 2

Em Am
The man said, "Why do you think you___ here?"

F A♭
I said, "I got no idea."

Em Am
I'm gonna, I'm gonna lose my baby,

F A♭
So I always keep a bottle near.

G7
He said, "I just think you're depressed,

F7
Kiss me, yeah baby, and go rest."

Chorus 3

C7
They tried to make me go to rehab, I said, "No, no, no."

Yes, I've been black but when I come back you'll know, know, know.

Verse 3

Em Am
I don't ever wanna drink___ again,

F A♭
I just, ooh, I just need a friend.

Em Am
I'm not gonna spend ten weeks,

F A♭
Have everyone think I'm on the mend.

G7
And it's not just my pride,

F7
It's just till these tears have dried.

Chorus 4

C7
They tried to make me go to rehab, I said, "No, no, no."

Yes, I've been black but when I come back you'll know, know, know.

G7 F7
I ain't got the time and if my daddy thinks I'm fine,

C7 F7 C7
He's tried to make me go to rehab, I won't go, go, go.

Senses Working Overtime

Words & Music by Andy Partridge

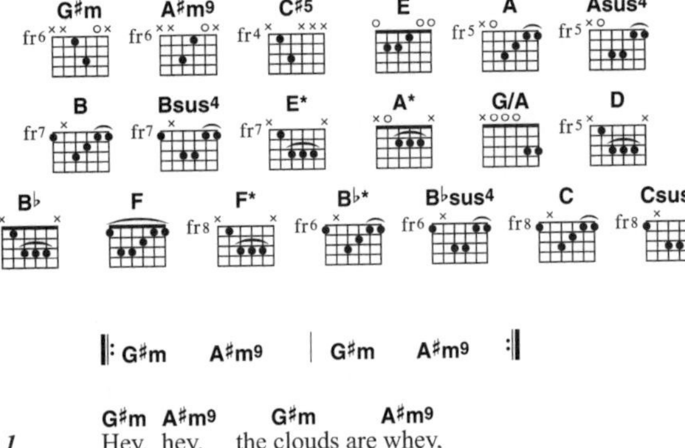

Intro ‖: G♯m A♯m9 | G♯m A♯m9 :‖

Verse 1

G♯m A♯m9 G♯m A♯m9
Hey, hey, the clouds are whey,

G♯m A♯m9
There's straw for the donkeys

G♯m A♯m9 C♯5 E C♯5
And the innocents can all sleep safe - ly,

E C♯5 E C♯5 E
All sleep safe - ly.

G♯m A♯m9 G♯m A♯m9
My, my, the sun is pie,

G♯m A♯m9
There's fodder for the cannons

G♯m A♯m9 C♯5 E C♯5
And the guilty ones can all sleep safe - ly,

E C♯5 E C♯5 E
All sleep safe - ly.

Pre-chorus 1

A Asus4 A
And all the world is football - shaped,

Asus4 B
It's just for me to kick its face,

Bsus4 B
And I can see, hear, smell, touch, taste,

E* B E*
And I've got one, two, three, four, five…

Chorus 1

```
N.C.                    A  E*   B
Senses working o - ver - time,
A           B           E*
Trying to take this all in.
B        E*          B            E*
I've got one, two, three, four, five
N.C.                    A  E*   B
Senses working o - ver - time,
A                        B                       A
Trying to taste the difference 'tween a lemon and a lime,
A          B                        E*
Pain and pleasure and the church bells softly chime.
```

Link 1

```
|: G#m   A#m9      | G#m    A#m9    :|
```

Verse 2

```
G#m    A#9  G#m          A#m9
   Hey hey, night fights day,
          G#m          A#m9
There's food for the thinkers
           G#m               A#m9   C#5   E  C#5
And the innocents can all live slow - ly,
E        C#5    E   C#5  E
All live slow - ly.
G#m   A#m9   G#m
   My, my, the sky will cry
G#m            A#m9
Jewels for the thirsty,
           G#m                 A#m9  C#  E       C#5
And the guilty ones can all die        slow - ly,
E       C#5    E   C#5  E
All die slow - ly.
```

Pre-chorus 2

```
A            Asus4             A
And all the world is biscuit - shaped,
             Asus4          B
It's just for me to feed my face.
            Bsus4                    B
And I can see, hear, smell, touch, taste
                E*          B          E*
And I've got one, two, three, four, five...
```

Chorus 2 As Chorus 1

Link 2

```
| A*  G/A | A*  G/A | A*  G/A | A*  G/A ||
```

```
              A*      G/A          A*       G/A         A* G/A      A*    G/A
Bridge          And birds might fall from black skies,        whoo, whoo,___

              A*      G/A          A*       G/A         A* G/A      A*    G/A
                And bullies might give you black eyes,       whoo, whoo,___

              A*        G/A        A*   G/A  D   A    D  A  D
                But to me they're very, very beau - ti - ful,___

              B♭ F                 B♭   F  B♭
                  (England's glo - ry,)

              D    A      D  A  D  B♭    F              B♭    F  B♭
              Beau - ti - ful,___     (A   striking beau - ty.)

              D          A          D        A       D
              Do do do do, do do do do, do do do,

              B♭               F*
              Do do do do, do do do do.


              B♭*              B♭sus4               B♭*
Pre-chorus 3    And all the world is football - shaped,

                             B♭sus4          C
              It's just for me to kick its face

                         Csus4                        C
              And I can see, hear, smell, touch, taste

                               F*          C          F*
              And I've got one, two, three, four, five…


              N.C.                 B♭* F*    C
Chorus 3      Senses working o  -  ver - time,

              B♭*       C         F*
              Trying to take this all in.

              C        F*        C          F*
              I've got one, two, three, four, five

              N.C.                 B♭* F*    C
              Senses working o  -  ver - time,

              B♭*                 C                             B♭*
              Trying to tell the difference 'tween the goods and grime,

              B♭*        C                        F*          C          F*
              Turds and treasure and there's one, two, three, four, five

              N.C.                 B♭* F*    C
              Senses working o  -  ver - time,

              B♭*       C         F*
              Trying to take this all in.

              C        F*        C          F*
              I've got one, two, three, four, five

              N.C.                 B♭* F*    C
              Senses working o  -  ver - time,

              B♭*                 C                       B♭*          C
              Trying to taste the difference 'tween a lemon and a lime,

              B♭*       C                  F*
              Pain and pleasure and the church bells softly chime.
```

Sir Duke

Words & Music by Stevie Wonder

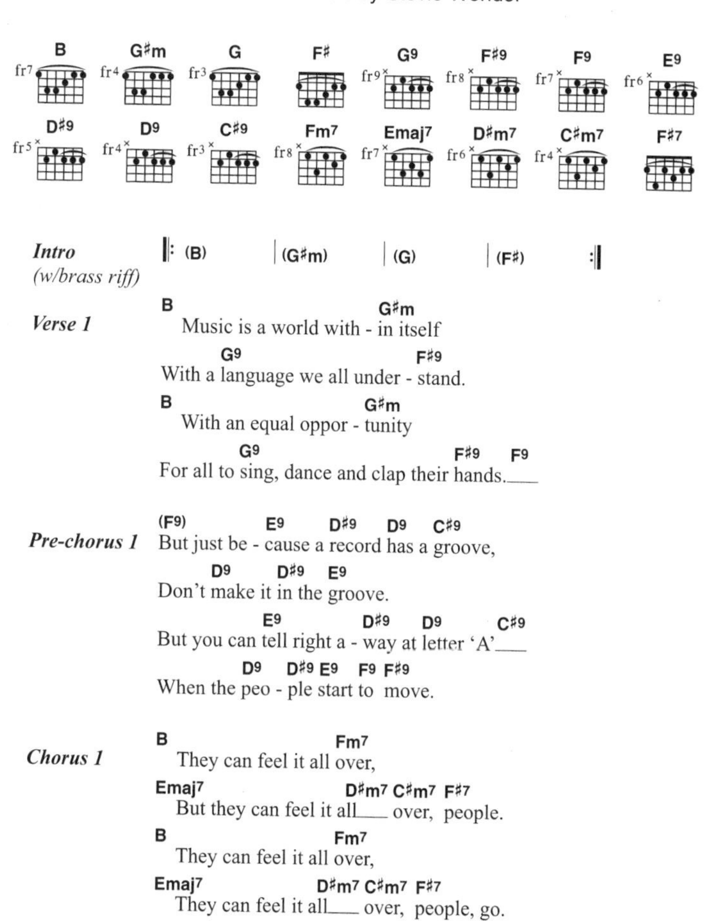

Intro
(w/brass riff)

𝄆 (B) | (G♯m) | (G) | (F♯) 𝄇

Verse 1

B G♯m
Music is a world with - in itself
G9 F♯9
With a language we all under - stand.
B G♯m
With an equal oppor - tunity
G9 F♯9 F9
For all to sing, dance and clap their hands.___

Pre-chorus 1

(F9) E9 D♯9 D9 C♯9
But just be - cause a record has a groove,
D9 D♯9 E9
Don't make it in the groove.
E9 D♯9 D9 C♯9
But you can tell right a - way at letter 'A'___
D9 D♯9 E9 F9 F♯9
When the peo - ple start to move.

Chorus 1

B Fm7
They can feel it all over,
Emaj7 D♯m7 C♯m7 F♯7
But they can feel it all___ over, people.
B Fm7
They can feel it all over,
Emaj7 D♯m7 C♯m7 F♯7
They can feel it all___ over, people, go.

Bridge 1

| N.C.(B) | N.C.(B) | N.C.(B) | N.C.(B) |

| N.C.(B) | N.C.(B) | N.C.(B) | N.C.(B) |

| N.C.(B) | N.C.(B) | N.C.(B) | N.C.(F♯) |

| N.C.(B) | N.C.(B) | N.C.(B) | N.C.(F♯) ||

Verse 2

B G♯m
Music knows it is and always will

G9 F♯9
Be one of the things that life just won't quit.

B G♯m
But here are some of music's pioneers

G9 F♯9 F9
That time will not allow us to for - get now.

Pre-chorus 2

(F9) E9 D♯9 D9 C♯9
For there's Basie, Miller, Satch - mo

D9 D♯9 E9
And the king of all Sir Duke.

E9 D♯9 D9 C♯9
And with a voice like Ella's ringing out

D9 D♯9 E9 F9 F♯9
There's no way the band could lose.

Chorus 2

B Fm7
You can feel it all over,

Emaj7 D♯m7 C♯m7 F♯7
You can feel it all___ over, people.

B Fm7
You can feel it all over,

Emaj7 D♯m7 C♯m7 F♯7
You can feel it all___ over, people.

Chorus 3 As Chorus 2

Bridge 2 As Bridge 1

Chorus 4 As Chorus 2

Chorus 5

```
B                          Fm7
   You can feel it all over,
Emaj7                      D#m7 C#m7 F#7
   You can feel it all___ over,  people.
B                          Fm7
   You can feel it all over,
Emaj7                           D#m7 C#m7         F#7
   I can feel it all over, all      over, all ov - er now people.
```

Chorus 6

```
B                            Fm7
   Can't you feel it all over?
Emaj7                    D#m7 C#m7   F#7
   Come on let's feel it all ov - er, people.
B                          Fm7
   You can feel it all over,
Emaj7               D#m7 C#m7 F#7
   Everybody all      over,  people, go.
```

Outro As Bridge 1

Shakin' All Over

Words & Music by Johnny Kidd

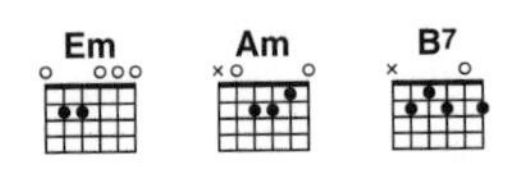

Intro | Em | Em | Em | Em ||

Verse 1
Em
When you move in right up close to me,

That's when I get the shakes all over me.

Chorus 1
Am
Quivers down my backbone,
Em
I got the shakes down my knee bone.
Am
Yeah, the tremors in my thigh bone,
Em
Shakin' all over.

| Em | Em | Em | Em ||

Verse 2
Em
Just the way that you say goodnight to me,

Brings that feelin' on inside of me.

Chorus 2

```
                          Am
Quivers down my backbone,
         Em
I got the shakes down my thigh bone.
         Am
Yeah, the tremors in my back bone,
Em
Shakin' all over.
```

Instrumental

```
| Em    | Em    | Em    | Em    |
| Am    | Am    | Em    | Em    |
| B7    | Am    | Em    | Em    | Em    ||
```

Chorus 3

```
                          Am
Quivers down the backbone,
         Em
Yeah, the shakes in the knee bone.
         Am
I got the tremors in the thigh bone,
Em
Shakin' all over.

| Em    | Em    ||
```

Outro

```
Em
Well, you make mc shake and I like it, baby,

Well, make me shake and I like it, baby,

Well, shake, shake, shake.
```

Sign Your Name

Words & Music by Terence Trent D'Arby

Em Asus2 D B7 B Am C G

Capo second fret

Intro |: Em | Em | Asus2 | Asus2 :| D | B7 ||

Verse 1

```
B                Am  B7
Fortunately you      have got
Em
Someone who relies on you.
   B               Am
We started out as friends
B7          Em
   But the thought of you just caves me in.
   B                   Am
The symptoms are so deep,
B7      Em
   It is much too late to turn away.
   B               Am      B7
We started out as friends.
```

Chorus 1

```
Em
Sign your name across my heart,
 Asus2
I want you to be my baby.
Em
Sign your name across my heart,
 Asus2                         D  B7
I want you to be my lady.
```

Verse 2

```
B                 Am
Time I'm sure will bring
B7          Em
   Disap - pointments in so many things.
  B                 Am
It seems to be the way,
B7              Em
   When your gambling cards on love you play.
   B              Am  B7         Em
I'd rather be in Hell     with you baby,
```

cont. Than in cool heaven.

B Am B7
It seems to be the way…

Chorus 2 As Chorus 1

Bridge

C G B7
Birds never look into the sun

Em
Before the day is gone.

C G
But oh the light shines brighter

B7
On a peaceful day.

C G B7
Stranger blue leave us a - lone

Em
We don't want to deal with you.

C G
We'll shed our stains showering

B7
In the room that makes the rain..

Instrumental ‖: Em | Em | Asus2 | Asus2 :‖ D | B7 ‖

Verse 3

B Am
All alone with you

B7 Em
Makes the butterflies in me arise.

B Am
Slowly we make love

B7 Em
And the Earth rotates to our dictates.

B Am B7 | N.C. | N.C. | N.C. | N.C. |
Slowly we make love.

Chorus 3

Em
‖: Sign your name across my heart,

Asus2
I want you to be my baby.

Em
Sign your name across my heart,

Asus2
I want you to be my lady. :‖ *Repeat to fade*

Solsbury Hill

Words & Music by Peter Gabriel

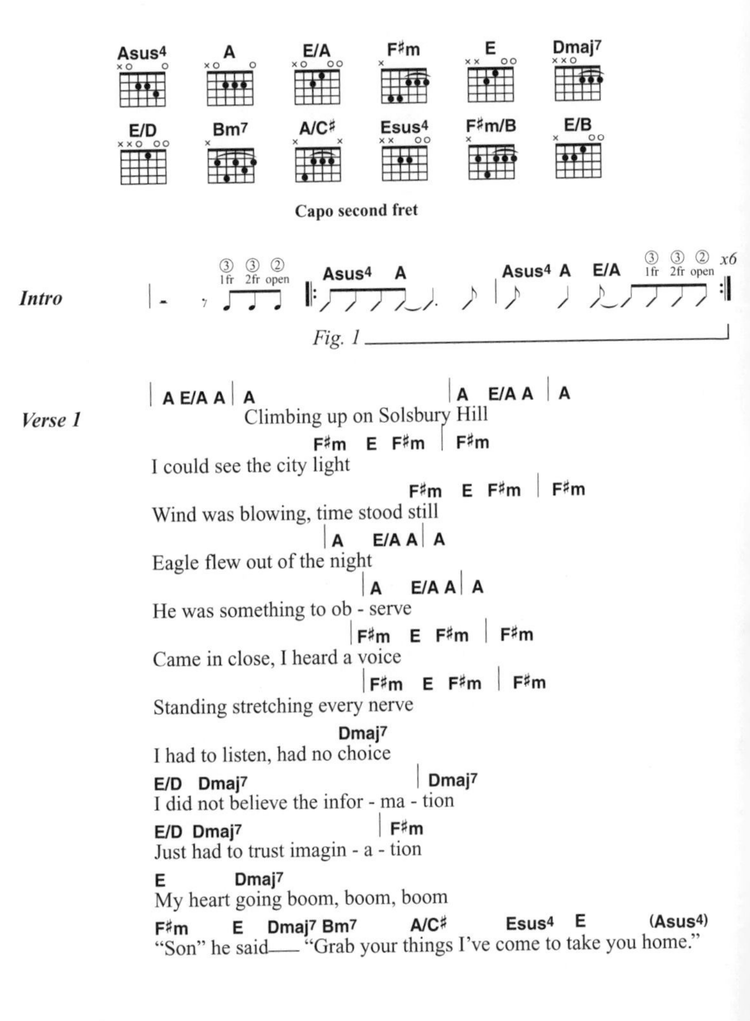

Link ‖: Asus4 A | Asus4 A E/A ③ 1fr ③ 2fr ② open :‖

Verse 2

| A E/A A | A | A E/A A | A

To keep in silence I res - igned

F♯m E F♯m | F♯m

My friends would think I was a nut

| F♯m E F♯m | F♯m

Turning water into wine

| A E/A A | A

Open doors would soon be shut

| A E/A A | A

So I went from day to day

| F♯m E F♯m | F♯m

Though my life was in a rut

| F♯m E F♯m | F♯m

Till I thought of what I'd say

| Dmaj7

Which connection I should cut

E/D Dmaj7 | Dmaj7

I was feeling part of the scene - ry

E/D Dmaj7 | F♯m

I walked right out of the machine - ry

E Dmaj7

My heart going boom, boom, boom

F♯m E Dmaj7 Bm7 A/C♯ Esus4 E Asus4 (fig.1)

"Hey" he said— "Grab your things I've come to take you home."

(Asus4)

Yeah, back home.

Link 2 ‖: Asus4 A | Asus4 A E/A ③ 1fr ③ 2fr ② open :‖ *Play 4 times*

Verse 3

| A E/A A | A | A E/A A | A
When illusion spin her net

| F♯m E F♯m | F♯m
I never where I wanna be

| F♯m E F♯m | F♯m
And liberty she pirou - ette

| A E/A A | A
When I think that I am free

| A E/A A | A
Watch my empty silhou - ette

| F♯m E F♯m | F♯m
Who close their eyes but still can see

| F♯m E F♯m | F♯m
No one taught them eti - quette

| Dmaj7
I will show another me

E/D Dmaj7 | Dmaj7
To - day I don't need a replace - ment

E/D Dmaj7 F♯m/B
I tell them what the smile on my face meant

E/B F♯m/B
My heart going boom, boom, boom

F♯m E Dmaj7 Bm7 A/C♯
"Hey" I said— "you can keep my things,

Esus4 E (Asus4)
they've come to take me home."

Outro

Asus4 A | Asus4 A E/A (③ 1fr ③ 2fr ② open) :‖ *Repeat to fade*

Stars

Words & Music by Mick Hucknall

Gsus2 G B7sus4 B7 Bm7 Am7

Intro ||: Gsus2 G | Gsus2 G | B7sus4 | B7 :||

Verse 1

```
G                   Bm7
  Anyone who ever held you
Am7                  B7sus4   B7
  Would tell you the way I'm feeling,
G                   Bm7
  Anyone who ever wanted you
Am7                             B7sus4        B7
  Would try to tell you what I feel     in - side.
G                         Bm7
  The only thing I ever wanted
Am7                      B7sus4    B7
  Was the feeling that you ain't faking,
G                           Bm7
  The only one you ever thought about,
Am7                    B7sus4 B7
  Wait a minute, can't you   see that
```

Chorus 1

```
G  Bm7            Am7
I——— wanna fall from the stars
B7sus4              B7
Straight into your    arms.
G  Bm7    Am7
I,——— I feel you,
 B7sus4               B7
I hope you compre - hend.
```

Link | Gsus2 G | Gsus2 G | B7sus4 B7 ||

Verse 2

```
G                              Bm7
   For the man who tried to hurt you,
Am7                        B7sus4  B7
   He's explaining the way I'm feeling.
G                         Bm7
   For all the jealousy I caused you
Am7                                B7sus4  B7
   States the reason why I'm trying to hide.
G                              Bm7
   As for all the things you taught me,
Am7                              B7sus4       B7
   It sends my future into clearer di - mensions.
G                           Bm7
   You'll never know how much you hurt me,
Am7                  B7sus4    B7
   Stay a minute, can't you see that
```

Chorus 2

```
G        Bm7                 Am7
I____          wanna fall from the stars
B7sus4                B7
Straight into your    arms.
G   Bm7    Am7
I,______ I feel you,
 B7sus4                B7
I hope you compre - hend.
```

Instrumental

| Gsus2 G | Gsus2 G | B7sus4 | B7 |

| Gsus2 G | Gsus2 G | B7sus4 | B7 |

| Gsus2 G | Gsus2 G | B7sus4 | B7 ||

Verse 3

```
G                          Bm7
   Too many hearts are broken,
Am7                                B7sus4      B7
   A lover's promise never came with a maybe.
G                                Bm7
So many words are left un - spoken,
Am7                        B7sus4     B7
   The silent voices are driving me crazy.
G                             Bm7
   After all the pain you        caused me,
Am7                             B7sus4           B7
   Making up could never be      your in - tention.
G                       Bm7
   You'll never know how much you hurt me,
Am7     B7sus4    B7
   Stay, can't you see that
```

Chorus 3

```
G   Bm7               Am7
I______ wanna fall from the stars
B7sus4             B7
Straight into your arms.
G   Bm7    Am7
I,______ I feel you,
  B7sus4               B7
I hope you compre - hend.
      G   Bm7                  Am7
That I______ wanna fall from the stars
B7sus4             B7
Straight into your arms.
G   Bm7    Am7
I,______ I feel you,
  B7sus4
I hope you comprehend.
```

Steady, As She Goes

Words & Music by Jack White & Brendan Benson

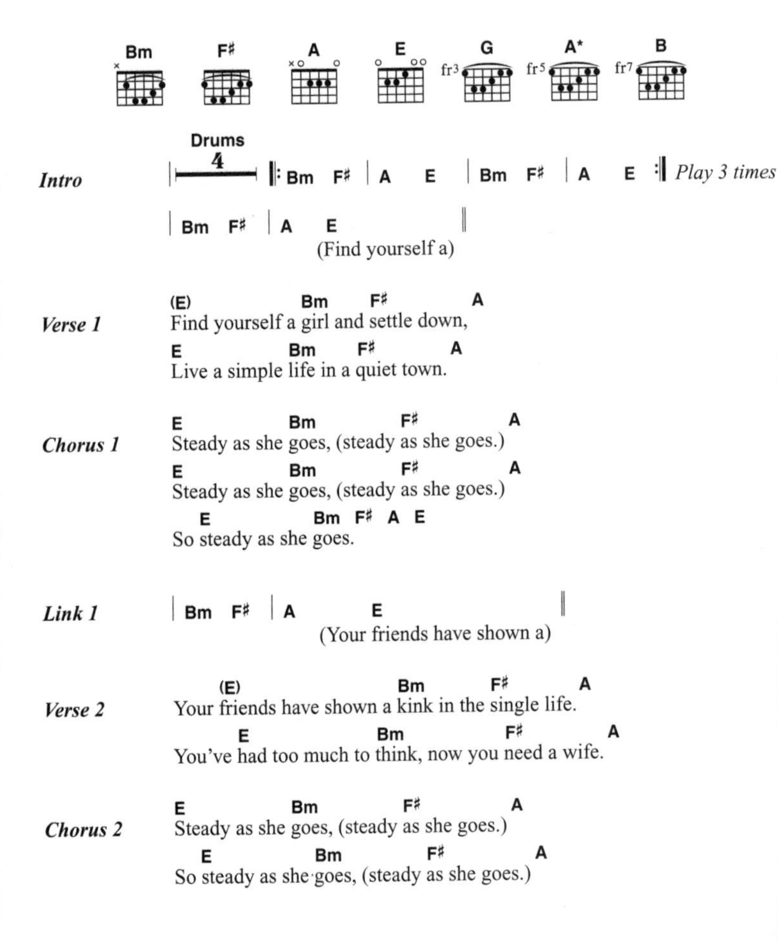

Bridge 1

```
           E              G
Well here we go a - gain,
                        A*                    B
You've found your - self a friend that knows you well.
                  A*         G
But no matter what you do,
                  A*                     E
You'll always feel as though you tripped and fell.
```

Chorus 3

```
                       Bm   F♯  A  E     Bm  F♯  A
So steady as she goes.
```

Verse 3

```
E                       Bm                F♯              A
When you have com - pleted what you thought you had to do,
E                       Bm             F♯             A
And your blood's de - pleted to the point of stable glue.
E                 Bm  F♯  A
Then you'll get a - long.
E                 Bm  F♯  A
Then you'll get a - long.
```

Chorus 4

```
E             Bm              F♯           A
Steady as she goes, (steady as she goes.)
   E             Bm              F♯           A
So steady as she goes, (steady as she goes.)
```

Bridge 2

```
           E              G
Well here we go a - gain,
                        A*                    B
You've found your - self a friend that knows you well.
                  A*         G
But no matter what you do,
                  A*                     E
You'll always feel as though you tripped and fell.
```

Chorus 5

```
                       Bm   F♯  A
So steady as she goes.
E             Bm  F♯
Steady as she goes.
```

Verse 4

```
E           Bm          F#          A
Settle for a girl, neither up or down.
E             Bm           F#             A
Sell it to the crowd that is gathered round.
E           Bm          F#          A
Settle for a girl, neither up or down.
E             Bm           F#             A   E
Sell it to the crowd that is gathered round.
```

Interlude

```
| Bm    | Bm    | Bm    | Bm    ||
```

Chorus 6

```
(Bm)              Bm           F#             A
So steady as she goes, (steady as she goes.)
E               Bm          F#          A
Steady as she goes, (steady as she goes.)
E               Bm          F#          A
Steady as she goes, (steady as she goes.)
   E              Bm           F#             A
So steady as she goes, (steady as she goes.)
```

Outro

```
E               Bm          F#          A
Steady as she goes, are you steady now?
E               Bm          F#          A
Steady as she goes, are you steady now?
E               Bm          F#          A
Steady as she goes, are you steady now?
E               Bm          F#          A
Steady as she goes, are you steady now?
E               Bm
Steady as she goes.
```

The Suburbs

Words & Music by Timothy Kingsbury, William Butler,
Richard Parry, Regine Chassagne & Win Butler

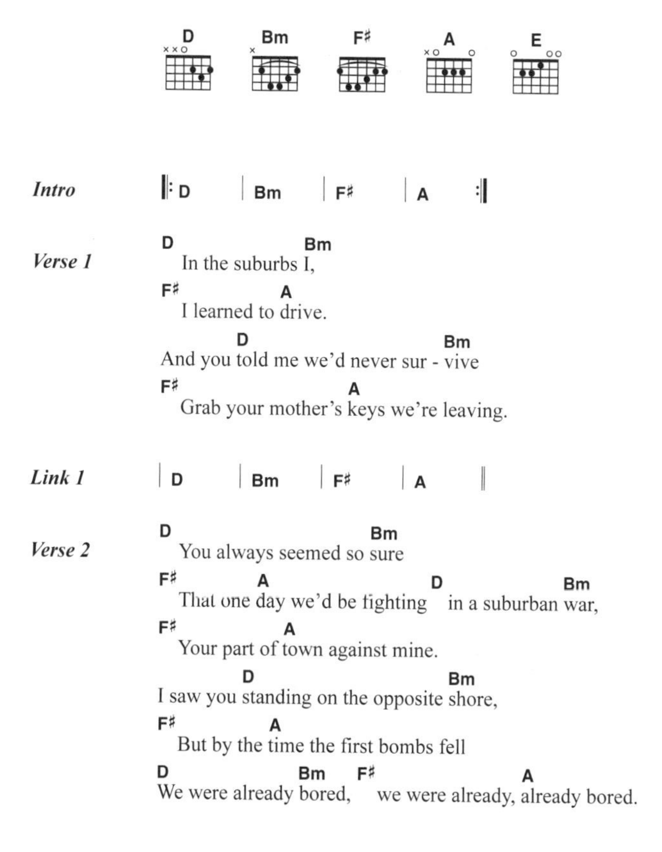

Intro

‖: D | Bm | F♯ | A :‖

Verse 1

```
D                 Bm
   In the suburbs I,
F♯             A
   I learned to drive.
               D                     Bm
And you told me we'd never sur - vive
F♯                        A
   Grab your mother's keys we're leaving.
```

Link 1

| D | Bm | F♯ | A ‖

Verse 2

```
D                               Bm
   You always seemed so sure
F♯            A                          D                 Bm
   That one day we'd be fighting   in a suburban war,
F♯                  A
   Your part of town against mine.
                 D                             Bm
I saw you standing on the opposite shore,
F♯              A
   But by the time the first bombs fell
D                         Bm       F♯                     A
We were already bored,     we were already, already bored.
```

Chorus 1

D Bm
Sometimes I can't believe it,
F♯ E
I'm moving past the feeling.
D Bm
Sometimes I can't believe it,
F♯ E (D)
I'm moving past the feeling a - gain.

Link 2

| D | Bm | F♯ | A ‖

Verse 3

D Bm
Kids wanna be so hard,
F♯ A D Bm
But in my dreams we're still screaming and running through the yard.
F♯ A D Bm
And all of the walls that they built in the seventies finally fall.
F♯ A D Bm
And all of the houses they built in the seventies finally fall.
F♯ A
Meant nothing at all, meant nothing at all, it meant nothing.

Chorus 2

D Bm
Sometimes I can't believe it,
F♯ E
I'm moving past the feeling.
D Bm
Sometimes I can't believe it,
F♯ E (D)
I'm moving past the feeling and into the night.

Link 3

‖: D | Bm | F♯ | A E :‖

Verse 4

D Bm
So can you under - stand
F♯ A D
Why I want a daughter while I'm still young?
Bm F♯ A
I wanna hold her hand and show her some beauty
D Bm
Be - fore this damage is done.
F♯ A D
But if it's too much to ask, if it's too much to ask,
Bm F♯ A
Then send me a son.

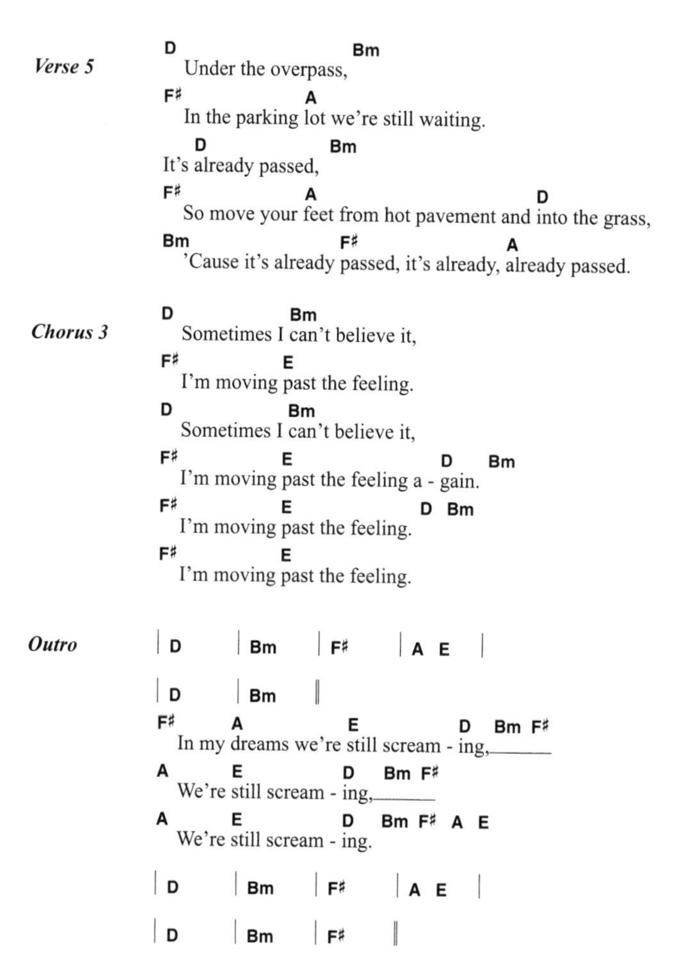

Verse 5

D Bm
Under the overpass,
F♯ A
In the parking lot we're still waiting.
D Bm
It's already passed,
F♯ A D
So move your feet from hot pavement and into the grass,
Bm F♯ A
'Cause it's already passed, it's already, already passed.

Chorus 3

D Bm
Sometimes I can't believe it,
F♯ E
I'm moving past the feeling.
D Bm
Sometimes I can't believe it,
F♯ E D Bm
I'm moving past the feeling a - gain.
F♯ E D Bm
I'm moving past the feeling.
F♯ E
I'm moving past the feeling.

Outro

| D | Bm | F♯ | A E |

| D | Bm ‖

F♯ A E D Bm F♯
In my dreams we're still scream - ing,______
A E D Bm F♯
We're still scream - ing,______
A E D Bm F♯ A E
We're still scream - ing.

| D | Bm | F♯ | A E |

| D | Bm | F♯ ‖

There Goes The Fear

Words & Music by Jez Williams, Andy Williams & Jimi Goodwin

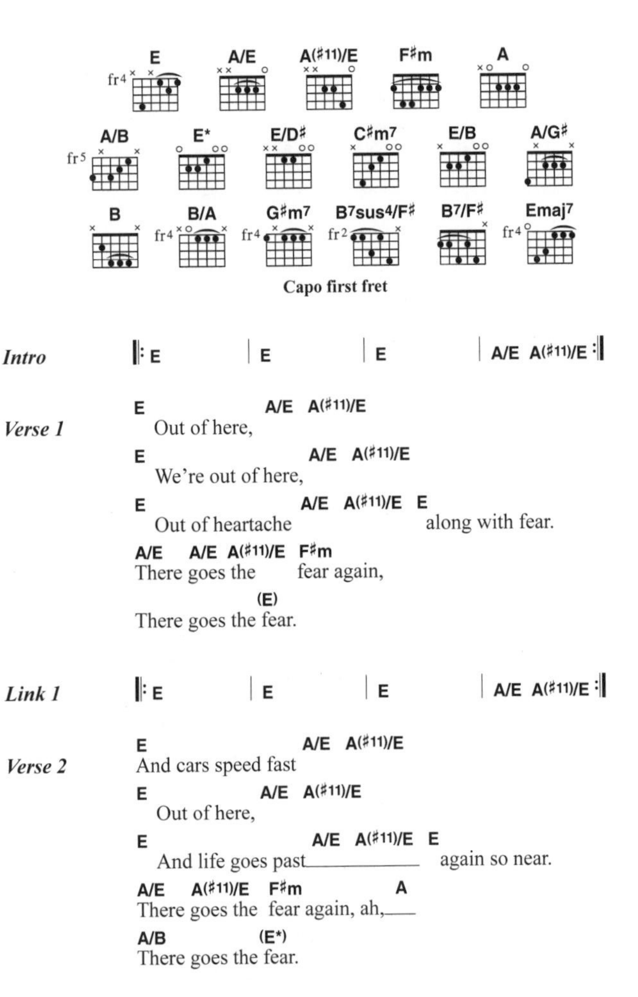

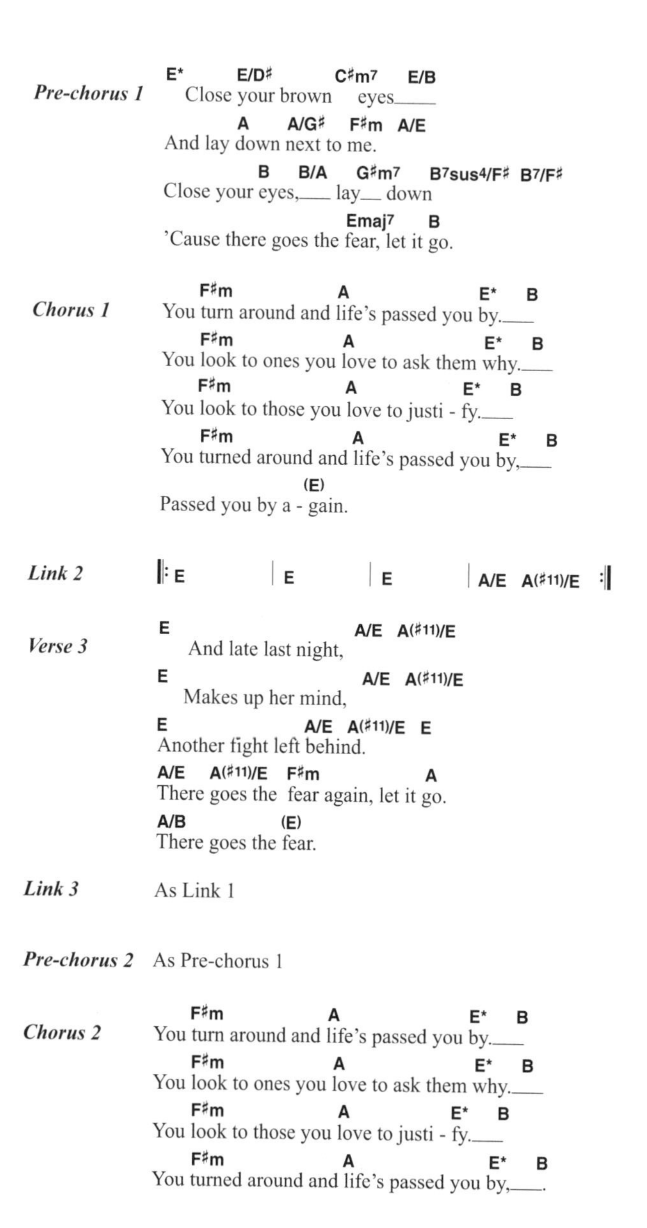

Pre-chorus 1

E* E/D♯ C♯m7 E/B
Close your brown eyes____

A A/G♯ F♯m A/E
And lay down next to me.

B B/A G♯m7 B7sus4/F♯ B7/F♯
Close your eyes,___ lay__ down

Emaj7 B
'Cause there goes the fear, let it go.

Chorus 1

F♯m A E* B
You turn around and life's passed you by.___

F♯m A E* B
You look to ones you love to ask them why.___

F♯m A E* B
You look to those you love to justi - fy.___

F♯m A E* B
You turned around and life's passed you by,___

(E)
Passed you by a - gain.

Link 2

|: E | E | E | A/E A(♯11)/E :|

Verse 3

E A/E A(♯11)/E
And late last night,

E A/E A(♯11)/E
Makes up her mind,

E A/E A(♯11)/E E
Another fight left behind.

A/E A(♯11)/E F♯m A
There goes the fear again, let it go.

A/B (E)
There goes the fear.

Link 3 As Link 1

Pre-chorus 2 As Pre-chorus 1

Chorus 2

F♯m A E* B
You turn around and life's passed you by.___

F♯m A E* B
You look to ones you love to ask them why.___

F♯m A E* B
You look to those you love to justi - fy.___

F♯m A E* B
You turned around and life's passed you by,___.

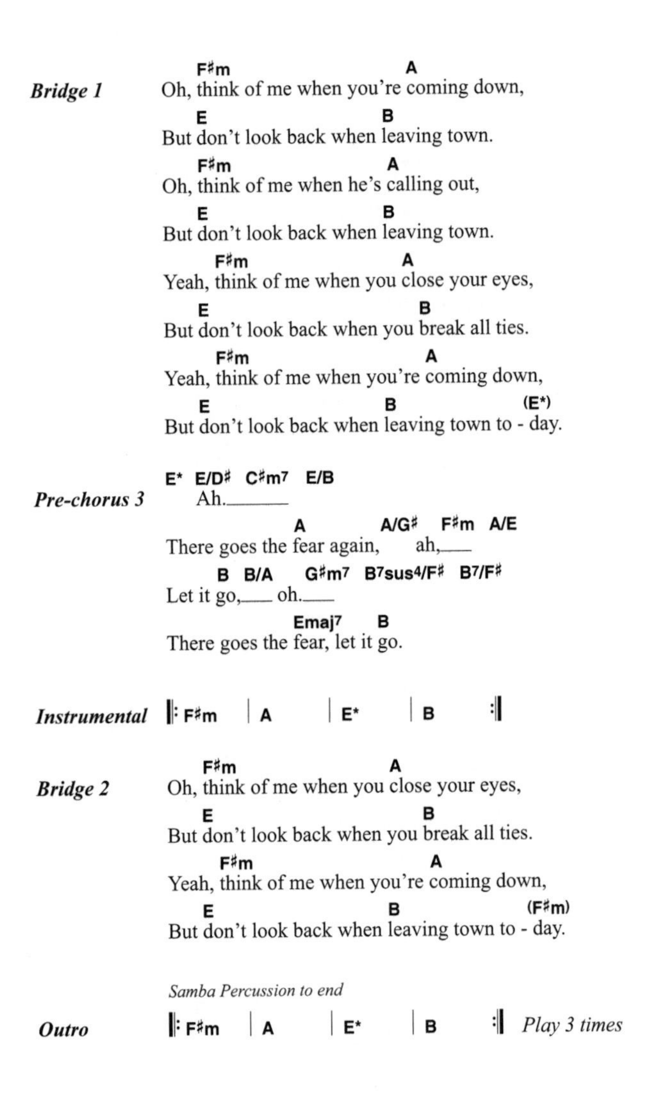
Bridge 1
F♯m A
Oh, think of me when you're coming down,
E B
But don't look back when leaving town.
F♯m A
Oh, think of me when he's calling out,
E B
But don't look back when leaving town.
F♯m A
Yeah, think of me when you close your eyes,
E B
But don't look back when you break all ties.
F♯m A
Yeah, think of me when you're coming down,
E B (E*)
But don't look back when leaving town to - day.
Pre-chorus 3
E* E/D♯ C♯m7 E/B
Ah.
A A/G♯ F♯m A/E
There goes the fear again, ah,
B B/A G♯m7 B7sus4/F♯ B7/F♯
Let it go, oh.
Emaj7 B
There goes the fear, let it go.
Instrumental
F♯m A E* B
Bridge 2
F♯m A
Oh, think of me when you close your eyes,
E B
But don't look back when you break all ties.
F♯m A
Yeah, think of me when you're coming down,
E B (F♯m)
But don't look back when leaving town to - day.
Samba Percussion to end
Outro
F♯m A E* B
Play 3 times

This Ain't A Love Song

Words & Music by Roy Stride

C G/B Am7 Gsus4 G F Am F(add9)

Intro | C | G/B | Am7 | Gsus4 ||

Verse 1

```
C
  Every night I remember that evening,
G/B
  The way you looked when you said you were leaving,
Am7                                     G
  The way you cried as you turned to walk a - way.
C
  The cruel words and the false accusations,
G/B
  The mean looks and the same old frustrations,
Am7                                   G
  I never thought that we'd throw it all a - way,
                   (F)
But we threw it all a - way.
```

Chorus 1

```
F               Am7               Gsus4
  And I'm a little bit lost with - out you,
                                 F
And I'm a bloody big mess in - side.
                Am                Gsus4
And I'm a little bit lost with - out you,
                                   F(add9)  Am7  Gsus4
This ain't a love song, this is good - bye.
                                   F(add9)  Am7  Gsus4
This ain't a love song, this is good - bye.
```

Verse 2

```
C
  I've been lost, I've been out, I've been losing,
G/B
  I've been tired, I'm all hurt and confusion,
Am7                                          Gsus4
  I've been mad, I'm the kind of man that I'm not.
C
  I'm going down, I'll be coming back fighting,
G/B
  I may be scared and a little bit frightened,
Am7                                   Gsus4
But I'll be back, I'll be coming back to life,
                         (F)
I'll be coming back to life.
```

Chorus 2 As Chorus 1

Bridge

```
Gsus4 F              C              G
  Oh,     and you can try, (you can try)
                                C            F
And you can try but you'll never keep me down.
                C           G
And you can try, (you can try)
                                C
And you can try but you'll never keep me down.
```

Interlude

```
| C      | G/B    | Am7    | Gsus4  |
C              G/B          Am
   La la la la,     la la la la la.
               Gsus4          (F)
I won't be lost, I won't be down.
```

Chorus 3

```
F               Am                  G
  And I'm a little bit lost with - out you,

And I'm a bloody big mess inside.
F               Am                  Gsus4
  And I'm a little bit lost with - out you,
                                    (F)
This ain't a love song, this is good - bye.
```

```
Outro    F         C
           It's all right,
         G                               C     G/B     F
           'Cause you can try but you'll never keep me down.
               C
         It's all right,
         G                         C     G/B     F
           I may be lost but you'll never keep me down.
                 C
         You can try,
         G                        C     G/B     F
           You can try but you'll never keep me down.
                 C
         You can try,
         G                           C         G/B  F
           I know I'm lost but I'm waiting to be found.
         C  G        C     G/B     F
              You'll never keep me down.
         C  G        C     G/B     F
              You'll never keep me down.
         C  G       G/B      F      C  G  C
              Never keep me down.
```

This Old Heart Of Mine (Is Weak For You)

Words & Music by Brian Holland, Freddie Gorman, Robert Bateman, Georgia Dobbins & William Garrett

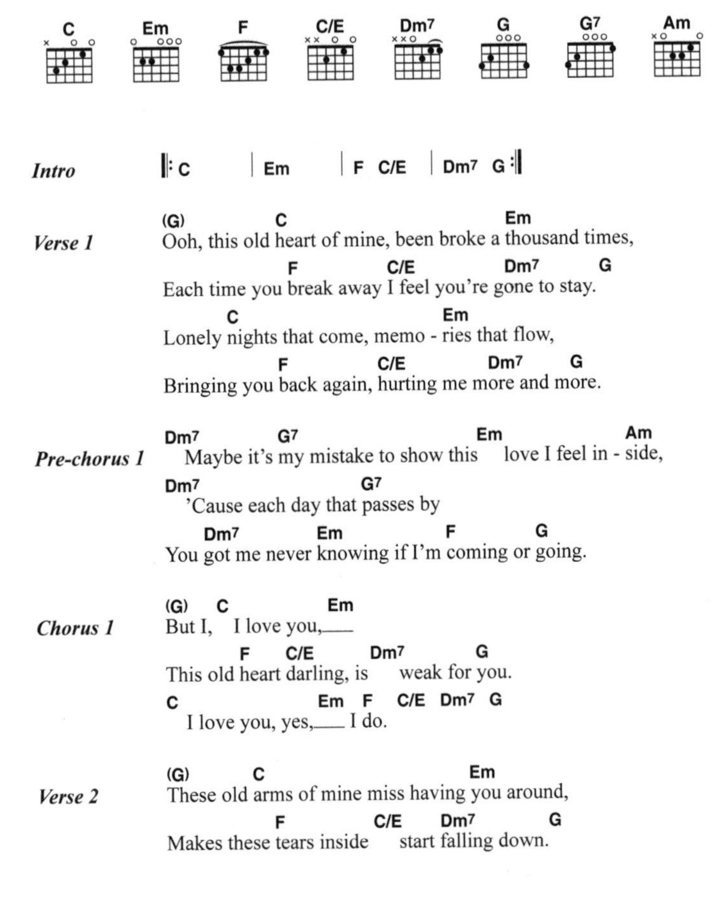

Intro | : C | Em | F C/E | Dm7 G : |

Verse 1

(G) C Em
Ooh, this old heart of mine, been broke a thousand times,
F C/E Dm7 G
Each time you break away I feel you're gone to stay.
C Em
Lonely nights that come, memo - ries that flow,
F C/E Dm7 G
Bringing you back again, hurting me more and more.

Pre-chorus 1

Dm7 G7 Em Am
Maybe it's my mistake to show this love I feel in - side,
Dm7 G7
'Cause each day that passes by
Dm7 Em F G
You got me never knowing if I'm coming or going.

Chorus 1

(G) C Em
But I, I love you,___
F C/E Dm7 G
This old heart darling, is weak for you.
C Em F C/E Dm7 G
I love you, yes,___ I do.

Verse 2

(G) C Em
These old arms of mine miss having you around,
F C/E Dm7 G
Makes these tears inside start falling down.

Pre-chorus 2

Dm7 G7 Em Am
Always with half a kiss you re - mind me of what I miss.
Dm7 G7
Though I try to con - trol myself,
Dm7 Em F G
Like a fool I start grinning 'cause my head starts spinning.

Chorus 2

(G) C Em
'Cause I, I love you,___
F C/E Dm7 G
This old heart darling, is weak for you.
C Em F C/E Dm7 G
I love you,___ yes, I do, yes I do.

Instrumental

| C | Em | F C/E | Dm7 G ||

Verse 3

(G) C Em
Ooh, I try hard to hide my hurt inside,
F C/E Dm7 G
This old heart of mine always keeps me cry - ing.
C Em
The way you're treating me leaves me incomplete,
F C/E Dm7 G
You're here for the day, gone for the week, now.

Pre-chorus 3

Dm7 G7
But if you leave me a hundred times,
Em Am
A hundred times I'll take you back.
Dm7 G7
I'm yours when - ever you want me,
Dm7 Em F G
I'm not too proud to shout it, tell the world a - bout it.

Chorus 3

(G) C Em
'Cause I, I love you,___
F C/E Dm7 G
This old heart darling, is weak for you.
C Em
I love you,___
F C/E Dm7 G
This old heart darling, is weak for you.
C Em
I love you,___
F C/E Dm7 G
This old heart darling, is weak for you.
C Em F C/E Dm7 G
I love you,___ yes, I do, yes I do.
C Em F C/E Dm7 G
I love you,___ yes, I do, yes I do. *To fade*

Tonight's The Night

Words & Music by Rod Stewart

Cmaj7 Dm7 Fm C A7sus4 E B Emaj7

fr7 fr7

Amaj7 F♯ E/G♯ F♯/A♯ G♯m7 C♯m7 D G

fr4 fr4 fr4 fr5 fr3

Intro | Cmaj7 | Dm7 | Fm | C |
| A7sus4 | E ||

Verse 1

B   Emaj7
Stay away from my window,
B   Emaj7
Stay away from my back door too.
B   Emaj7
Disconnect the telephone line,
B   Emaj7   Amaj7 F♯ E/G♯ F♯/A♯
Relax baby and draw that blind.

Verse 2

B   Emaj7
Kick off your shoes and sit right down,
B   Emaj7
Loosen off that pretty French gown.
B   Emaj7
Let me pour you a good long drink,
B   Emaj7
Ooh, baby don't you hesitate.

Chorus 1

(Emaj7) B   Emaj7
'Cause   tonight's the night,
B   G♯m7
It's gonna be all right,
          C♯m7
'Cause I love you girl,
           E   B   F♯
Ain't no - body gonna stop us now.

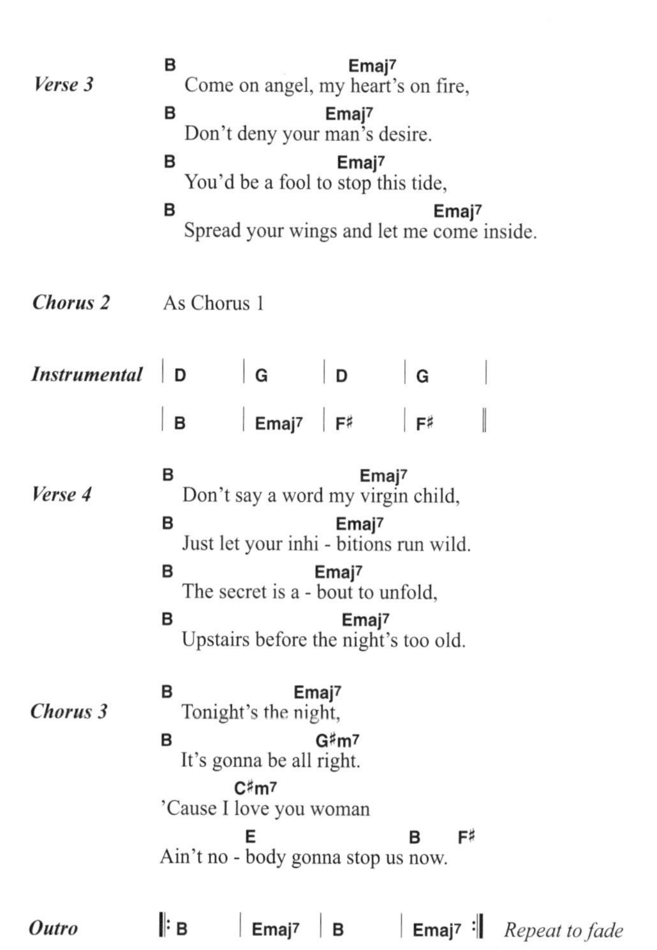

Verse 3

B Emaj7
Come on angel, my heart's on fire,
B Emaj7
Don't deny your man's desire.
B Emaj7
You'd be a fool to stop this tide,
B Emaj7
Spread your wings and let me come inside.

Chorus 2 As Chorus 1

Instrumental | D | G | D | G |

| B | Emaj7 | F♯ | F♯ ||

Verse 4

B Emaj7
Don't say a word my virgin child,
B Emaj7
Just let your inhi - bitions run wild.
B Emaj7
The secret is a - bout to unfold,
B Emaj7
Upstairs before the night's too old.

Chorus 3

B Emaj7
Tonight's the night,
B G♯m7
It's gonna be all right.
C♯m7
'Cause I love you woman
E B F♯
Ain't no - body gonna stop us now.

Outro |: B | Emaj7 | B | Emaj7 :| *Repeat to fade*

The Tracks Of My Tears

Words & Music by William "Smokey" Robinson,
Warren Moore & Marvin Tarplin

G C D G/B Am D/F♯ C/E D7

```
Intro     | G        | C        | C          | D        |

          | G        | C        | C G/B  Am  | G        ||


                 G        C
          (Do do do do,   do do do do,
                G       C          G/B  Am  G
          Do do do do,  do do do do  do   do.)

          G     C                    D
Verse 1   People say I'm the life of the party
          G           C              G/B  Am  G
          'Cause I tell a joke or two.
                                   C               D
          Although I might be laughing loud and hearty,
          G       C                G/B  Am  G
            Deep inside I'm blue.

          G                 C                D
Chorus 1  So take a good look at my face,
                          G     C                   D
          You'll see my smile   looks out of place.
                        G      C               D
          If you look closer, it's easy to trace
                        G                 C  G/B  Am  G
          The tracks___ of my tears.___

          (G)   C       G               C        G
Link 1    I need you, (need you) need you, (need you)

          G     C                                   D
Verse 2   Since you left me if you see me with another girl,
          G              C                  G/B  Am  G
          Seeming like I'm having fun.
```

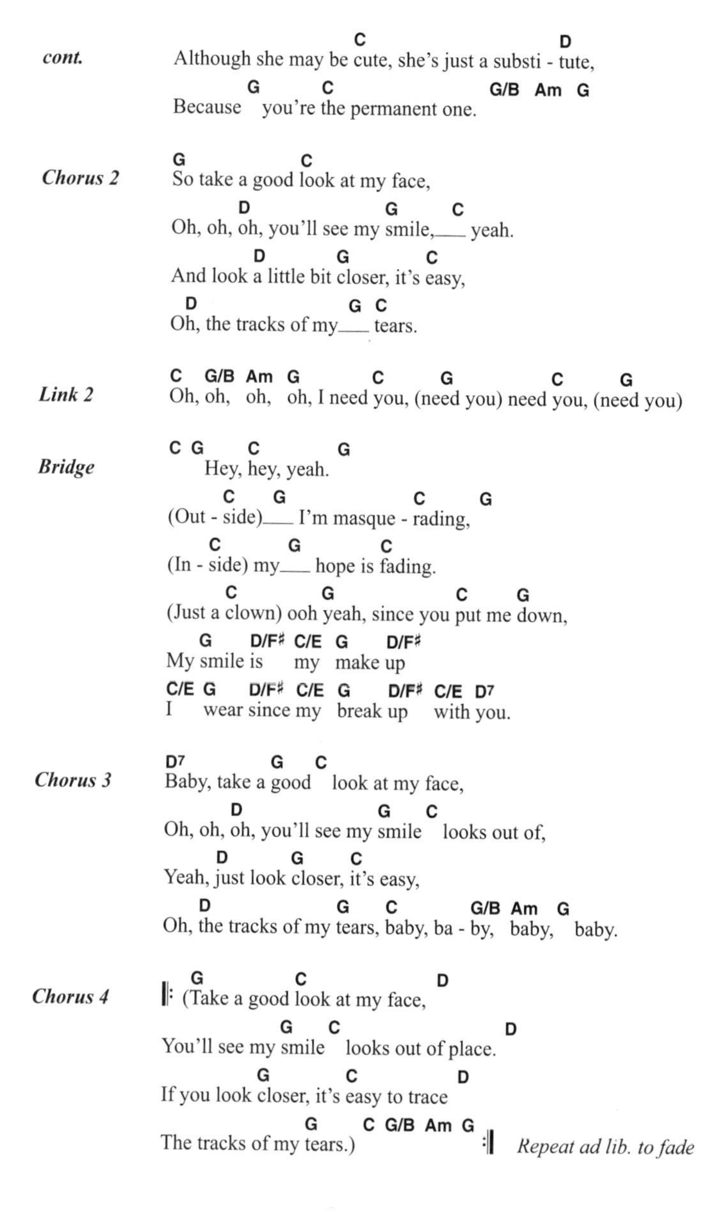

cont.

C D
Although she may be cute, she's just a substi - tute,
G C G/B Am G
Because you're the permanent one.

Chorus 2

G C
So take a good look at my face,
D G C
Oh, oh, oh, you'll see my smile,___ yeah.
D G C
And look a little bit closer, it's easy,
D G C
Oh, the tracks of my___ tears.

Link 2

C G/B Am G C G C G
Oh, oh, oh, oh, I need you, (need you) need you, (need you)

Bridge

C G C G
Hey, hey, yeah.
C G C G
(Out - side)___ I'm masque - rading,
C G C
(In - side) my___ hope is fading.
C G C G
(Just a clown) ooh yeah, since you put me down,
G D/F♯ C/E G D/F♯
My smile is my make up
C/E G D/F♯ C/E G D/F♯ C/E D7
I wear since my break up with you.

Chorus 3

D7 G C
Baby, take a good look at my face,
D G C
Oh, oh, oh, you'll see my smile looks out of,
D G C
Yeah, just look closer, it's easy,
D G C G/B Am G
Oh, the tracks of my tears, baby, ba - by, baby, baby.

Chorus 4

G C D
𝄆 (Take a good look at my face,
G C D
You'll see my smile looks out of place.
G C D
If you look closer, it's easy to trace
G C G/B Am G
The tracks of my tears.) 𝄇 *Repeat ad lib. to fade*

Up On The Roof

Words & Music by Carole King & Gerry Goffin

Intro

N.C. A♭6
Up on the roof.

Up on the roof.

Verse 1

A♭6 Fm7
When this old world starts getting me down
D♭ B♭m7 E♭7 A♭6
And people are just too much for me to face.
Fm7
I climb way up to the top of the stairs,
D♭ B♭m7 E♭7 A♭6
And all my cares just drift right into space.

Bridge 1

D♭ D♭6 D♭maj7 D♭6
On the roof it's peaceful as can be,
A♭6 Fm7 D♭6 E♭7
And there the world be - low can't bother me.

Let me tell you now.

Verse 2

A♭6 Fm7
When I come home feeling tired and beat,
D♭ B♭m7 E♭7 A♭6
I go up where the air is fresh and sweet.
Fm7
I get away from the hustling crowd
D♭ B♭m7 E♭7 A♭6
And all that rat-race noise down in the street.

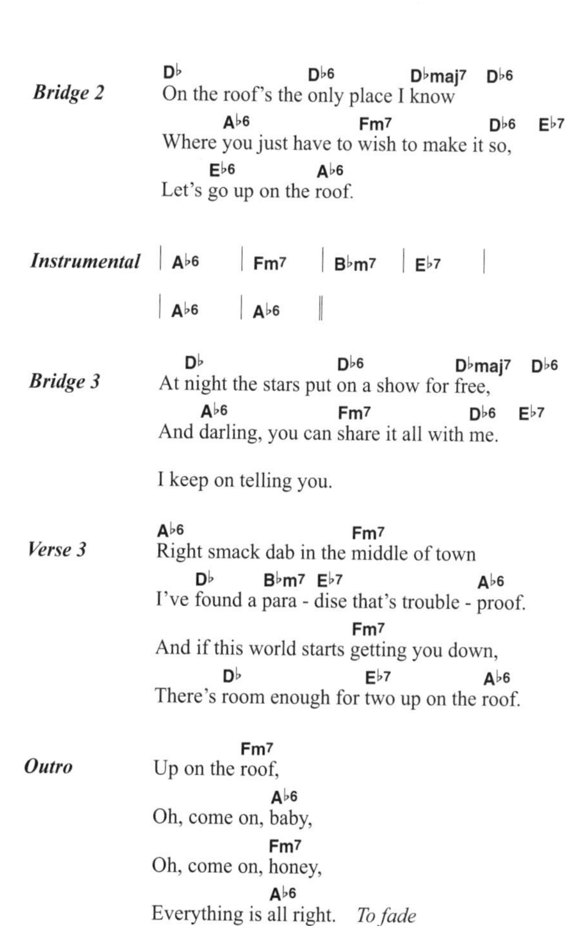

Bridge 2

D♭ D♭6 D♭maj7 D♭6
On the roof's the only place I know
A♭6 Fm7 D♭6 E♭7
Where you just have to wish to make it so,
E♭6 A♭6
Let's go up on the roof.

Instrumental

| A♭6 | Fm7 | B♭m7 | E♭7 |
| A♭6 | A♭6 ||

Bridge 3

D♭ D♭6 D♭maj7 D♭6
At night the stars put on a show for free,
A♭6 Fm7 D♭6 E♭7
And darling, you can share it all with me.

I keep on telling you.

Verse 3

A♭6 Fm7
Right smack dab in the middle of town
D♭ B♭m7 E♭7 A♭6
I've found a para - dise that's trouble - proof.
Fm7
And if this world starts getting you down,
D♭ E♭7 A♭6
There's room enough for two up on the roof.

Outro

Fm7
Up on the roof,
A♭6
Oh, come on, baby,
Fm7
Oh, come on, honey,
A♭6
Everything is all right. *To fade*

Valerie

Words & Music by Sean Payne, David McCabe,
Boyan Chowdhury, Russell Pritchard & Abigail Harding

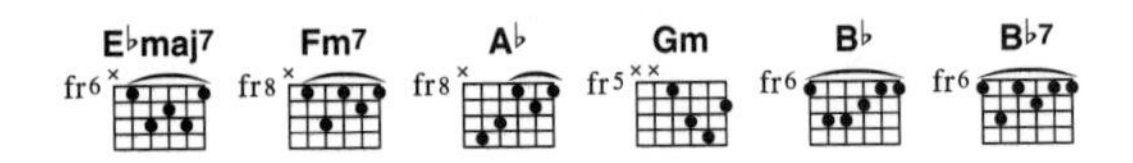

Verse 1

N.C. E♭maj7
Well, some - times I go out by myself

Fm7
And I look across the water.

E♭maj7
And I think of all the things, what you're doing

Fm7
And in my head I paint a picture.

Chorus 1

A♭
Well, since I've come-a home,

Gm
Well my body's been a mess,

A♭
And I've missed your ginger hair

Gm
And the way you like to dress.

A♭
Won't you come on over,

Gm B♭
Stop making a fool out of me,

B♭7 E♭maj7
Why don't you come on over, Valerie?

Fm7
Vale - rie.

E♭maj7
Valerie.

Fm7
Vale - rie.

Verse 2

(Fm7) E♭maj7
Did you have to go to jail, put your house on up for sale,
Fm7
Did you get a good lawyer?
E♭maj7
I hope you didn't catch a tan,
Fm7
I hope you find the right man who'll fix it for you.
E♭maj7
And are you shopping anywhere,
Fm7
Changed the colour of your hair, and are you busy?
E♭maj7
And did you have to pay that fine
Fm7
That you were dodging all the time are you still dizzy?

Chorus 2 As Chorus 1

Verse 3 As Verse 1

Chorus 3 As Chorus 1

Outro

(Fm7) E♭maj7
Whoa, Valerie.
Fm7
Oh, Vale - rie.
E♭maj7 Fm7
Oh, Valerie, Valerie, yeah, Vale - rie.
A♭ E♭maj7
Oh, why don't you come on over, Vale - rie?

Warwick Avenue

Words & Music by James Hogarth, Aimee Duffy & Francis Eg White

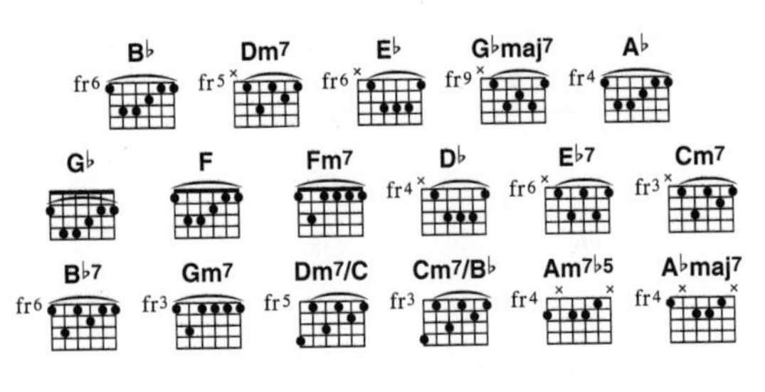

Intro | B♭ | Dm7 | E♭ | G♭maj7 ||

Verse 1

(G♭maj7) B♭ Dm7
When I get to Warwick Ave - nue,
E♭ G♭maj7
Meet me by the entrance of the tube.
B♭ Dm7
We can talk things over a little time,
E♭ G♭maj7
Promise me you won't stand by the light.
B♭ Dm7
When I get to Warwick Ave - nue,
E♭ G♭maj7
Please drop the past and be true.
B♭ Dm7
Don't think we're okay just because I'm here,
A♭ G♭ F
You hurt me bad but I won't shed a tear.

```
               B♭        Fm7        D♭           E♭7
Chorus 1     I'm leaving you for the last time ba - by,
             Cm7               B♭7          A♭        Gm7
               You think you're loving but you don't love me.
              Cm7          Gm7        Fm7
             I've been con - fused, out of my mind lately,
             E♭  N.C.                           Dm7 Dm7/C  Gm7
               You think you're loving but I want to be    free,
                  Cm7          B♭
             Baby, you've hurt me.

Link 1       | B♭      | Dm7     | E♭      | G♭maj7 ||

             (G♭maj7) B♭                Dm7
Verse 2      When I   get to Warwick Ave - nue,
                             E♭                     G♭maj7
             We'll spend an hour but no more than two.
                        B♭                  Dm7
             Our only chance to speak once more,
                                E♭                      G♭maj7
             I showed you the answers, now here's the door.
                     B♭                  Dm7
             When I get to Warwick Ave - nue,
                         A♭             G♭        F
             I'll tell you baby that we're through.

               B♭        Fm7        D♭           E♭7
Chorus 2     I'm leaving you for the last time ba - by,
             Cm7               B♭7          A♭        Gm7
               You think you're loving but you don't love me.
              Cm7          Gm7        Fm7
             I've been con - fused, out of my mind lately,
             E♭  N.C.                              Dm7 Dm7/C  Gm7
               You think you're loving but you don't love    me,
              Cm7            Fm7  E♭          B♭
             I want to be free, baby, you've hurt me.
```

```
             Cm7    Cm7/B♭          Am7♭5                 A♭maj7
Bridge       All the days spent to - gether, I wished for better,

                 Gm7                       Cm7
             But I didn't want the train to come.

                 Cm7/B♭  Am7♭5                 A♭maj7
             Now it's de  -  parted, I'm broken hearted,

                  Gm7
             Seems like we never started.

             Cm7                         Fm7                         A♭
             All those days spent to - gether when I wished for better,

                  Gm7                            G♭     F
             And I didn't want the train to come.___


Instrumental | B♭   Fm7   | D♭   E♭7   | Cm7   B♭7  |

             | A♭   Gm7   | Cm7  Cm7/B♭ | Fm7       ||


             E♭  N.C.                                Dm7  Dm7/C   Gm7
Outro           You think you're loving but you don't love me,

              Cm7        Fm7        E♭         B♭
             I want to be free, baby, you hurt me.

                Dm7  Dm7/C  Gm7  Cm7        Fm7
             You don't love    me, I want to be free,

                 E♭          B♭
             Baby, you've hurt me.
```

We Gotta Get Out Of This Place

Words & Music by Barry Mann & Cynthia Weil

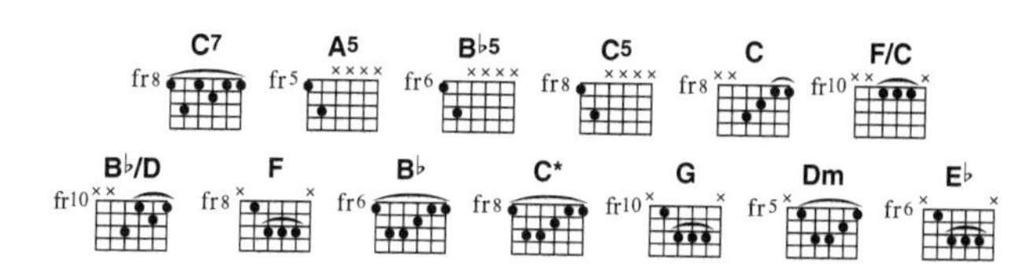

Intro | N.C.(C7) | N.C.(C7) | N.C.(C7) | N.C.(C7) ||

```
               N.C.(C7)
Verse 1        In this dirty old part of the city

               Where the sun refused to shine,
                                                   A5  B♭5  C5
               People tell me there ain't no use in tryin'.
                                                   A5  B♭5  C5
               Now my girl you're so young and pretty
                                       A5  B♭5  C5
               And one thing I know is true,
                                          A5  B♭5 C5
               You'll be dead before your time is   due, I know.
               C F/C C                        C   F/C  C
                      Watch my daddy in bed a - dy - in',
                                          C F/C  C
               Watched his hair been turnin' grey,
                                               C   F/C C
               He's been workin' and slavin' his life a  -  way,

               Oh yes, I know.
```

Pre-chorus 1

B♭/D F/C C B♭/D F/C C
(Yeah.) He's been work - in' so hard.
B♭/D F/C C
(Yeah.) I've been workin' too, baby.
B♭/D F/C C
(Yeah.) Every night and day,

(Yeah, yeah, yeah, yeah.)

Chorus 1

F B♭ C*
We gotta get out of this place
F G C*
If it's the last thing we ever do.
F B♭ C*
We gotta get out of this place,
Dm (F)
'Cause girl, there's a better life for me and you.

Link

| F E♭ | B♭ C* | F E♭ | B♭ C* ||

Verse 2

C7 A5 B♭5 C5
Now my girl you're so young and pretty
A5 B♭5 C5
And one thing I know is true, yeah,
A5 B♭5 C5
You'll be dead before your time is due, I know it.
C F/C C C F/C C
Watch my daddy in bed a - dy - in',
C F/C C
Watched his hair been turnin' grey, yeah,
C F/C C
He's been workin' and slavin' his life a - way,

I know he's been workin' so hard.

Pre-chorus 2

B♭/D F/C C B♭/D F/C
(Yeah.) I've been workin' too, baby.
C B♭/D F/C
(Yeah.) Every day baby.
C B♭/D F/C C
(Yeah.) Whoa.________

(Yeah, yeah, yeah, yeah!)

Chorus 2

```
F                  B♭          C*
   We gotta get out of this place
F                              G    C*
   If it's the last thing we ever do.
F                  B♭          C*
   We gotta get out of this place,
Dm
Girl, there's a better life for me and you.
F  E♭  B♭       C              F  E♭         B♭     C
          Some - where baby,         some - how I know it.
```

Chorus 3

```
F                  B♭          C*
   We gotta get out of this place
F                              G    C*
   If it's the last thing we ever do.
F                  B♭          C*
   We gotta get out of this place,
Dm                                            (F)
Girl, there's a better life for me and you.
F  E♭     B♭    C
     Be - lieve me baby.
F   E♭             B♭  C
   I know it baby,
                  F  E♭  B♭  C
You know it too.
```

What's Going On

Words & Music by Marvin Gaye, Al Cleveland & Renaldo Benson

Emaj7 (fr7) C♯m7 (fr4) F♯m7 (fr2) Bsus4 (fr2) B13 Am7 (fr5) B7

Intro | Emaj7 | Emaj7 | Emaj7 | Emaj7 ||

Verse 1

Emaj7
Mother, mother,
C♯m7
There's too many of you crying.
Emaj7
Brother, brother, brother,
C♯m7
There's far too many of you dying.
F♯m7
You know we've got to find a way
B7sus4 B13
To bring some lovin' here today, yeah.

Verse 2

Emaj7
Father, father,
C♯m7
We don't need to escalate.
Emaj7
You see, war is not the answer,
C♯m7
For only love can conquer hate.
F♯m7
You know we've got to find a way
B7sus4 B13
To bring some lovin' here today, oh.

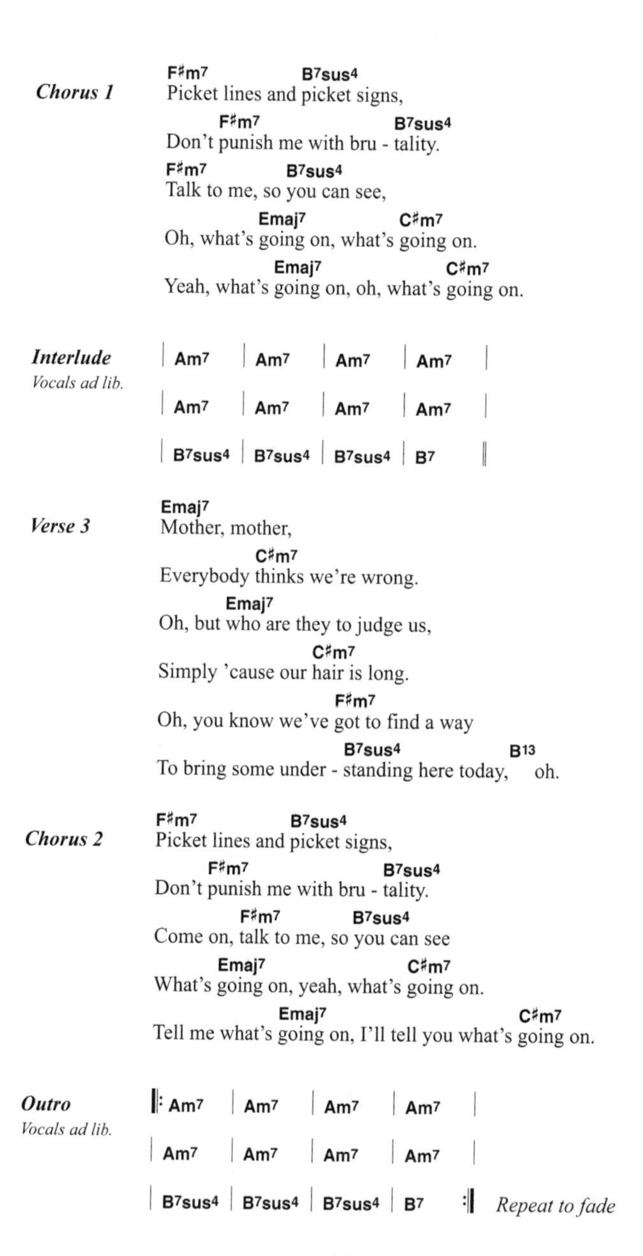

Chorus 1

F♯m7 B7sus4
Picket lines and picket signs,
F♯m7 B7sus4
Don't punish me with bru - tality.
F♯m7 B7sus4
Talk to me, so you can see,
Emaj7 C♯m7
Oh, what's going on, what's going on.
Emaj7 C♯m7
Yeah, what's going on, oh, what's going on.

Interlude
Vocals ad lib.

Am7	Am7	Am7	Am7
Am7	Am7	Am7	Am7
B7sus4	B7sus4	B7sus4	B7	

Verse 3

Emaj7
Mother, mother,
C♯m7
Everybody thinks we're wrong.
Emaj7
Oh, but who are they to judge us,
C♯m7
Simply 'cause our hair is long.
F♯m7
Oh, you know we've got to find a way
B7sus4 B13
To bring some under - standing here today, oh.

Chorus 2

F♯m7 B7sus4
Picket lines and picket signs,
F♯m7 B7sus4
Don't punish me with bru - tality.
F♯m7 B7sus4
Come on, talk to me, so you can see
Emaj7 C♯m7
What's going on, yeah, what's going on.
Emaj7 C♯m7
Tell me what's going on, I'll tell you what's going on.

Outro
Vocals ad lib.

||: Am7 | Am7 | Am7 | Am7 |
| Am7 | Am7 | Am7 | Am7 |
| B7sus4 | B7sus4 | B7sus4 | B7 :|| *Repeat to fade*

Whip It

Words & Music by Mark Mothersbaugh & Gerald Casale

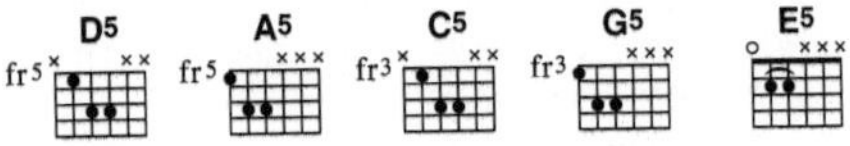

D5 A5 C5 G5 E5

Intro

riff 1
‖: E 0fr ⑥ E 0fr ⑥ A 5fr ⑥ B 7fr ⑥ D 5fr ⑤ | D5 A5 | riff 1 | D5 A5 :‖

Verse 1

riff 1 D5 A5 riff 1 D5 A5
Crack that whip, give the past the slip.
riff 1 D5 A5 riff 1 D5 A5 riff 1 D5 A5
Step on a crack, break your mama's back.
riff 1 D5 A5
When a problem comes along you must whip it.
riff 1 D5 A5
Before the cream sits out too long you must whip it.
riff 1 D5 A5
When something's going wrong you must whip it.

Chorus 1

C5 G5
Now whip it into shape,
D5 C5
Shape it up, get straight.
G5
Go forward, move ahead,
D5 C5
Try to detect it, it's not too late

To whip it, whip it good.

Link 1

| riff 1 | D5 A5 ‖

Verse 2

```
(A5)     riff 1                            D5              A5
When a good time turns around you must whip it.
              riff 1                       D5             A5
You will never live it down un - less you whip it.
riff 1                        D5                A5
No one gets away un - til they whip it.
```

Bridge

```
E5 G5 C5
          I say whip it,
E5 G5 C5
          Whip it good.
E5 G5 C5
          I say whip it,
E5 G5 C5
          Whip it good.
```

Interlude

```
  riff 2_______________________________
|: E    E    A    B    D    A    A    G    F#  :|   Play 8 times
   0fr  0fr  5fr  7fr  5fr  5fr  5fr  3fr  2fr
   ⑥    ⑥    ⑥    ⑥    ⑤    ⑥    ⑥    ⑥    ⑥
```

Verse 3

As Verse 1

Chorus 2

```
C5              G5
   Now whip     it into shape,
D5                C5
   Shape it up,     get straight.
              G5
Go forward,     move ahead,
D5                   C5
   Try to detect it,     it's not too late
               G5
To whip it,     into shape,
D5                C5
   Shape it up,     get straight.
              G5
Go forward,     move ahead,
D5                   C5
   Try to detect it,     it's not too late

To whip it, whip it good.
```

Outro

```
| riff 1   | D5  A5 | riff 1   ||
```

Whole Lotta Shakin' Goin' On

Words & Music by David Williams

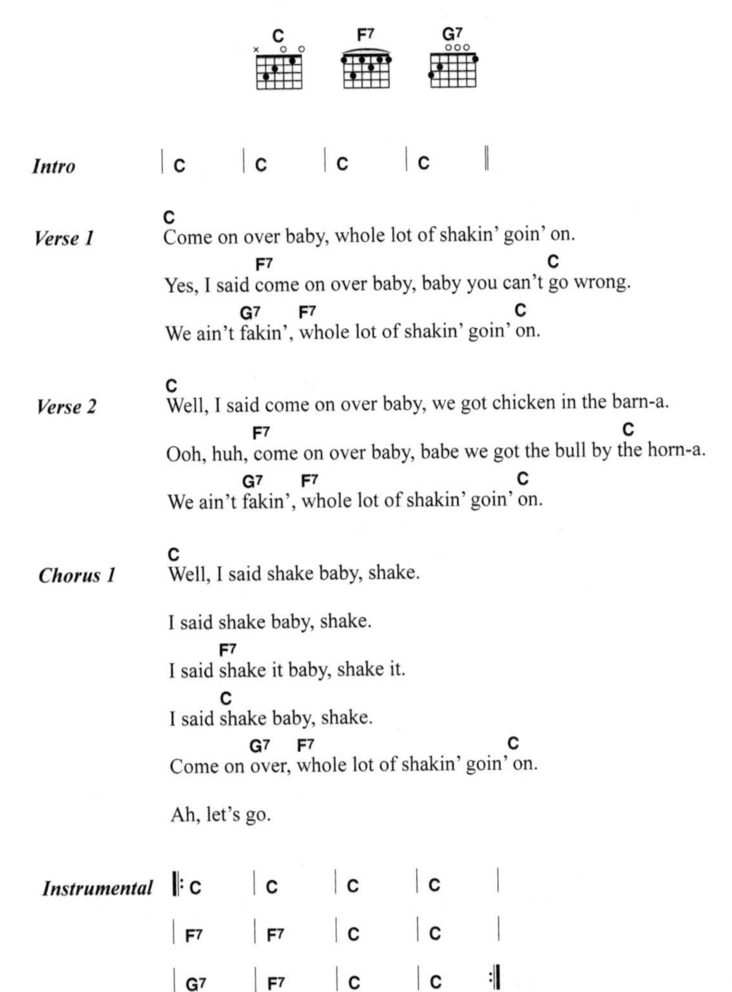

Intro | C | C | C | C ||

Verse 1

C
Come on over baby, whole lot of shakin' goin' on.
F7 C
Yes, I said come on over baby, baby you can't go wrong.
G7 F7 C
We ain't fakin', whole lot of shakin' goin' on.

Verse 2

C
Well, I said come on over baby, we got chicken in the barn-a.
F7 C
Ooh, huh, come on over baby, babe we got the bull by the horn-a.
G7 F7 C
We ain't fakin', whole lot of shakin' goin' on.

Chorus 1

C
Well, I said shake baby, shake.

I said shake baby, shake.
F7
I said shake it baby, shake it.
C
I said shake baby, shake.
G7 F7 C
Come on over, whole lot of shakin' goin' on.

Ah, let's go.

Instrumental |: C | C | C | C |
| F7 | F7 | C | C |
| G7 | F7 | C | C :|

Verse 3

C
Well, I said come on over baby, we got chicken in the barn

Who's barn, what barn? My barn.

F7 C
Come on over baby well, we got the bull by the horns.

G7 F7 C
We ain't fakin', whole lot of shakin' goin' on.

Chorus 2

C
Easy now,

Shake it, ah, shake it baby.

F7 C
Yeah, you can shake it one time for me.

G7 F7 C
Well, I said come over baby, whole lot of shakin' goin' on.

Chorus 3

C
Now let's get real low one time now.

Shake baby, shake.

All you gotta do honey is kinda stand in one spot,

F7
Wiggle around just a little bit,

C
That's what you gotta do, yeah.

G7 F7 C
Oh baby, whole lotta shakin' goin' on.

Chorus 4

C
Now let's go one time.

Shake it baby, shake it.

I said shake it baby, shake it.

F7
Ooh, shake baby, come on babe.

C
Shake baby, shake it.

G7 F7 C
Come on over, whole lot of shakin goin' on.

Wild Thing

Words & Music by Chip Taylor

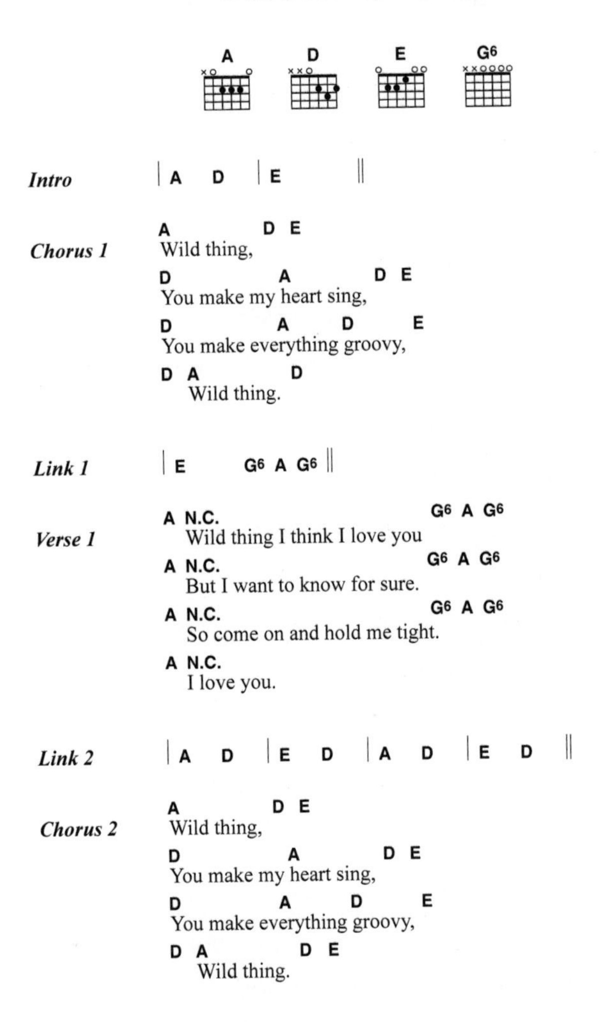

Intro | A D | E ||

Chorus 1

A D E
Wild thing,
D A D E
You make my heart sing,
D A D E
You make everything groovy,
D A D
Wild thing.

Link 1 | E G6 A G6 ||

Verse 1

A N.C. G6 A G6
Wild thing I think I love you
A N.C. G6 A G6
But I want to know for sure.
A N.C. G6 A G6
So come on and hold me tight.
A N.C.
I love you.

Link 2 | A D | E D | A D | E D ||

Chorus 2

A D E
Wild thing,
D A D E
You make my heart sing,
D A D E
You make everything groovy,
D A D E
Wild thing.

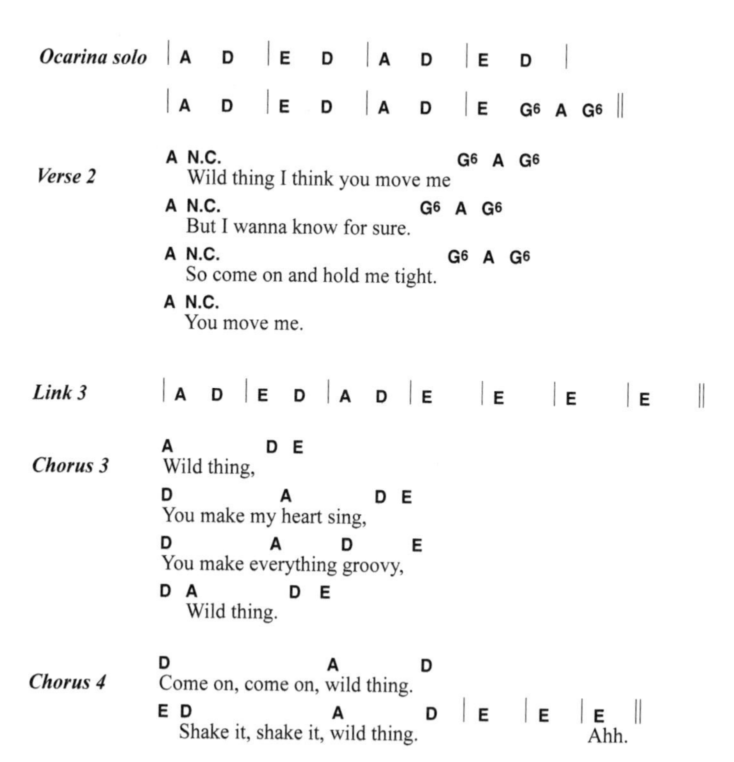

Ocarina solo | A D | E D | A D | E D |

| A D | E D | A D | E G6 A G6 ||

Verse 2

A N.C. G6 A G6
Wild thing I think you move me

A N.C. G6 A G6
But I wanna know for sure.

A N.C. G6 A G6
So come on and hold me tight.

A N.C.
You move me.

Link 3 | A D | E D | A D | E | E | E | E ||

Chorus 3

A D E
Wild thing,

D A D E
You make my heart sing,

D A D E
You make everything groovy,

D A D E
Wild thing.

Chorus 4

D A D
Come on, come on, wild thing.

E D A D | E | E | E ||
Shake it, shake it, wild thing. Ahh.

Will You Love Me Tomorrow

Words & Music by Carole King & Gerry Goffin

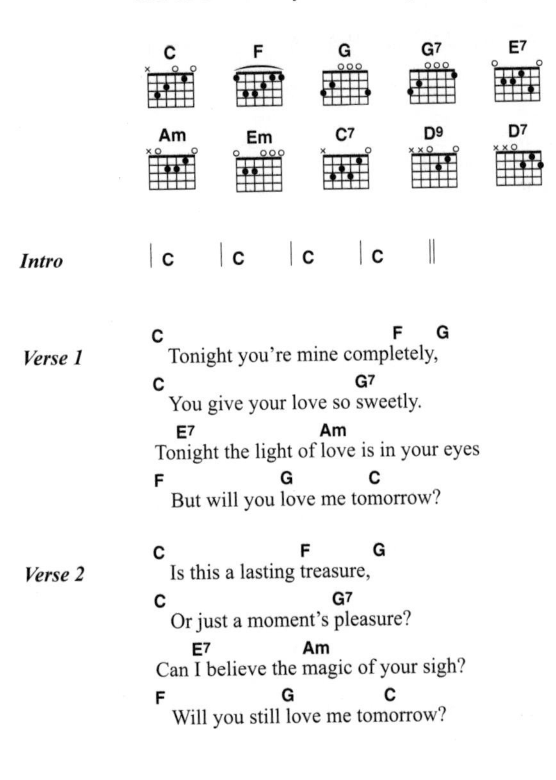

Intro | C | C | C | C ||

Verse 1

```
C                                  F    G
   Tonight you're mine completely,
C                              G7
   You give your love so sweetly.
   E7                   Am
Tonight the light of love is in your eyes
F                 G          C
   But will you love me tomorrow?
```

Verse 2

```
C                        F         G
   Is this a lasting treasure,
C                           G7
   Or just a moment's pleasure?
      E7              Am
Can I believe the magic of your sigh?
F                 G              C
   Will you still love me tomorrow?
```

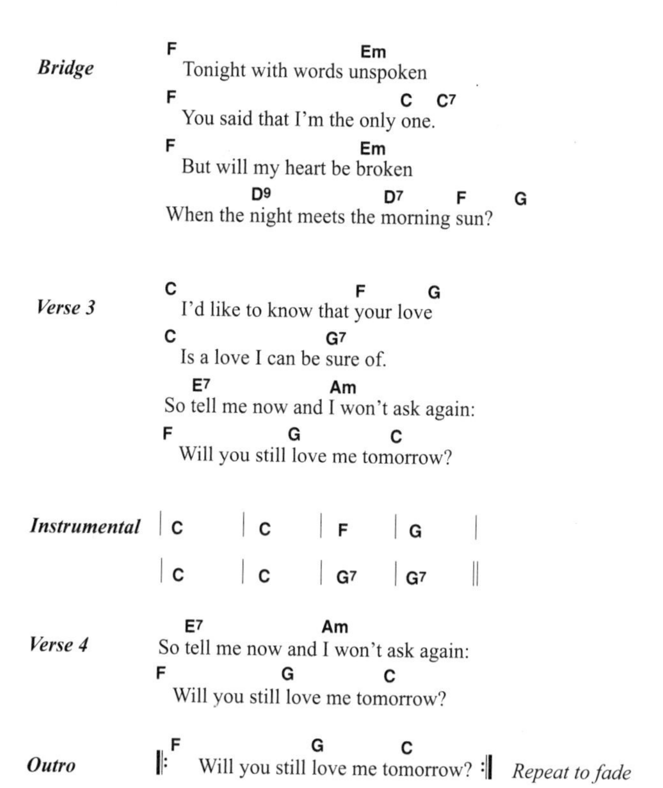
Bridge
F Em
Tonight with words unspoken
F C C7
You said that I'm the only one.
F Em
But will my heart be broken
D9 D7 F G
When the night meets the morning sun?
Verse 3
C F G
I'd like to know that your love
C G7
Is a love I can be sure of.
E7 Am
So tell me now and I won't ask again:
F G C
Will you still love me tomorrow?
Instrumental
| C | C | F | G |
| C | C | G7 | G7 ||
Verse 4
E7 Am
So tell me now and I won't ask again:
F G C
Will you still love me tomorrow?
Outro
F G C
Will you still love me tomorrow?
Repeat to fade

You To Me Are Everything

Words & Music by Ken Gold & Michael Denne

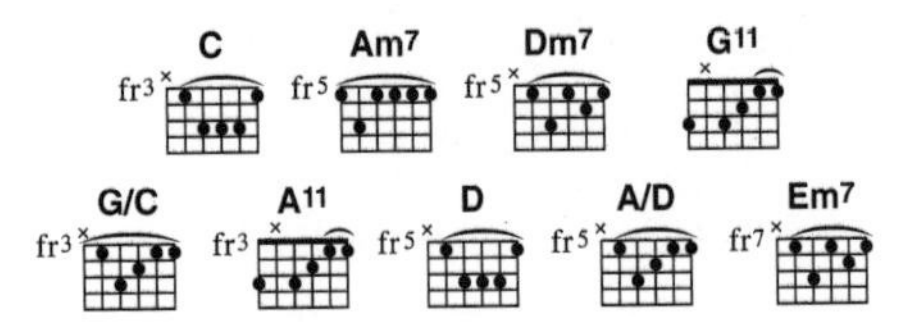

To match original recording, tune guitar slightly flat

Intro 𝄆 C | Am7 | Dm7 | G11 𝄇

Verse 1

C
I would take the stars out of the sky for you,
Am7
Stop the rain from falling if you asked me to.
Dm7 Am7
I'd do anything for you, your wish is my command,
Dm7 G11
I could move a mountain when your hand is in my hand.

Verse 2

C
Words cannot express how much you mean to me,
Am7
There must be some other way to make you see.
Dm7 Am7
If it takes my heart and soul you know I'd pay the price,
Dm7 G11
Everything that I possess I'd gladly sacrifice.

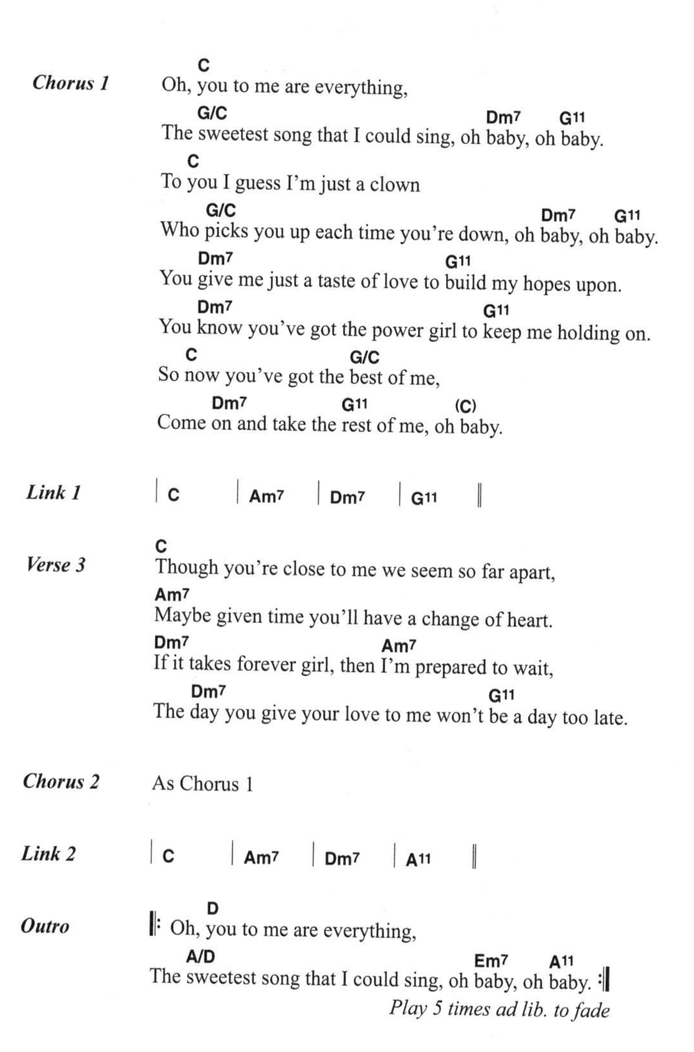

Chorus 1

C
Oh, you to me are everything,
G/C Dm7 G11
The sweetest song that I could sing, oh baby, oh baby.
C
To you I guess I'm just a clown
G/C Dm7 G11
Who picks you up each time you're down, oh baby, oh baby.
Dm7 G11
You give me just a taste of love to build my hopes upon.
Dm7 G11
You know you've got the power girl to keep me holding on.
C G/C
So now you've got the best of me,
Dm7 G11 (C)
Come on and take the rest of me, oh baby.

Link 1

| C | Am7 | Dm7 | G11 ||

Verse 3

C
Though you're close to me we seem so far apart,
Am7
Maybe given time you'll have a change of heart.
Dm7 Am7
If it takes forever girl, then I'm prepared to wait,
Dm7 G11
The day you give your love to me won't be a day too late.

Chorus 2

As Chorus 1

Link 2

| C | Am7 | Dm7 | A11 ||

Outro

D
||: Oh, you to me are everything,
A/D Em7 A11
The sweetest song that I could sing, oh baby, oh baby. :||

Play 5 times ad lib. to fade

You've Lost That Lovin' Feelin'

Words & Music by Barry Mann, Cynthia Weil & Phil Spector

B♭/C C Dm Em F G Dm/C F/D

Capo first fret

Verse 1

```
N.C.        B♭/C                                   C
You never close your eyes anymore when I kiss your lips.
                B♭/C                               C
And there's no tenderness like before in your finger - tips.
               Dm                   Em)
You're trying hard not to show it, (baby)
     F    G
But baby, baby I know it.
```

Chorus 1

```
C                 Dm/C
   You've lost that lovin' feeling,
G            C
   Whoa, that lovin' feeling,
                 Dm/C
You've lost that lovin' feeling,
         B♭/C                C
Now it's gone, gone, gone, whoa, oh.
```

Verse 2

```
C                 B♭/C                                    C
Now there's no welcome look in your eyes when I reach for you.
                   B♭/C                         C
And now you're starting to criticise little things I do.
              Dm                  Em)
It makes me just feel like crying, (baby)
          F               G
'Cause baby, something beautiful's dying.
```

Chorus 2

```
C                 Dm/C
   You've lost that lovin' feeling,
G            C
   Whoa, that lovin' feeling,
                 Dm/C
You've lost that lovin' feeling,
         B♭/C                (C)
Now it's gone, gone, gone, whoa, oh.
```

Link 1 | C F | G F F/D ||

Bridge

C F G F F/D C F G F F/D
Baby, baby, I get down on my knees for you,

C F G F F/D C F G F F/D
If you would only love me like you used to do, yeah.

C F G F F/D C F G F F/D
We had a love, a love, a love you don't find every day,

C F G F F/D C F G F F/D
So don't, don't, don't, don't let it slip a - way.

C F G F
Baby, (baby), baby, (baby),

F/D C F G F
I beg you please, (please), please, (please),

F/D C F
I need your love, (I need your love),

G F
I need your love, (I need your love),

F/D C F
So bring it on back, (so bring it on back),

G F G
Bring it on back, (so bring it on back).

Chorus 3

C Dm/C
Bring back that lovin' feeling,

G C
Whoa, that lovin' feeling,

C Dm/C
Bring back that lovin' feeling,

B♭/C
'Cause it's gone, gone, gone,

(C)
And I can't go on, whoa, oh.

Link 2 | C F | G F F/D ||

Chorus 4

C Dm/C
Bring back that lovin' feeling,

G C
Whoa, that lovin' feeling,

C Dm/C
Bring back that lovin' feeling,

B♭/C
'Cause it's gone. *To fade*

You Can't Hurry Love

Words & Music by Brian Holland, Eddie Holland & Lamont Dozier

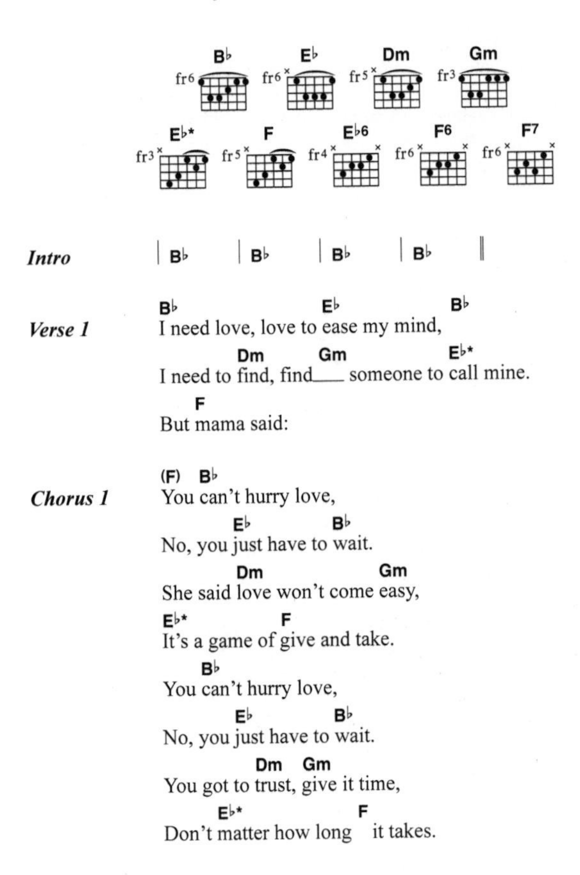

Intro | B♭ | B♭ | B♭ | B♭ ||

Verse 1

B♭ E♭ B♭
I need love, love to ease my mind,
Dm Gm E♭*
I need to find, find___ someone to call mine.
F
But mama said:

Chorus 1

(F) B♭
You can't hurry love,
E♭ B♭
No, you just have to wait.
Dm Gm
She said love won't come easy,
E♭* F
It's a game of give and take.
B♭
You can't hurry love,
E♭ B♭
No, you just have to wait.
Dm Gm
You got to trust, give it time,
E♭* F
Don't matter how long it takes.

Bridge 1

```
      Dm
But how many heartaches must I stand
            Gm
Before I find a love to let me live again.
                 E♭6
Right now the only thing that keeps me hanging on,
         F                  F6           F7
When I feel my strength,    yeah, it's almost gone,

I remember mama said:
```

Chorus 2

```
(F)  B♭
(You can't hurry love,)
           E♭           B♭
No, you just have to wait.
           Dm                Gm
She said love don't come easy,
E♭*              F
It's a game of give and take
    B♭
How long must I wait,
    E♭                   B♭
How much more can I take
        Dm       Gm
Before loneli - ness
      E♭*               F
Will cause my heart, heart to break?
```

Bridge 2

```
     Dm
No I can't bear to live my life alone,
                 Gm
I grow im - patient for a love to call my own.
                 E♭6
But when I feel that I, I can't go on,
          F               F6          F7
These precious words    keeps me hanging on,

I remember mama said:
```

Chorus 3

```
(F)  B♭
(You can't hurry love,)
           E♭           B♭
No, you just have to wait.
           Dm                Gm
She said love don't come easy,
E♭*              F
It's a game of give and take.
```

cont.

B♭
You can't hurry love,

E♭ B♭
No, you just have to wait.

Dm Gm
She said trust, give it time,

E♭* F B♭
No matter how long it takes. (Now, wait)

Verse 2

B♭ E♭ B♭
No, love, love, don't come easy.

Dm Gm E♭* F
But I keep on waiting, an - tici - pating

B♭ E♭ B♭
For that soft voice to talk to me at night,

Dm Gm E♭* F
For some tender arms to hold me tight.

B♭ E♭ B♭
I keep waiting, I keep on waiting,

Dm Gm E♭*
But it ain't easy,___ it ain't easy,

F
When mama said:

Chorus 4

(F) B♭
You can't hurry love,

E♭ B♭
No, you just have to wait

Dm Gm
She said trust, give it time,

E♭* F
No matter how long it takes.

B♭
You can't hurry love,

E♭ B♭
No, you just have to wait.

Dm Gm
She said love don't come easy,

E♭* F
It's a game of give and take.

B♭
You can't hurry love,

E♭ B♭
No, you can't hurry love. *To fade*

1 2 3 4 5 6 7 8 9